A SENSUAL GUIDE TO ORAL LOVEMAKING

WRITTEN BY

JACQUELINE & STEVEN FRANKLIN

PHOTOGRAPHED BY

CAESAR GUEST

MEDIAPRESS

Sexual Enrichment Series™

For All of Us.

Media Press
9135 Alabama Ave., Suite B, Chatsworth, CA 91311
Printed in the United States of America.

ISBN 0-917181-17-4

30 29 28 27 26 25 24 23

The ULTIMATE KISS

TABLE OF CONTENTS

MEDIAPRESS

INTRODUCTION

When Jacqueline and I were originally approached to write *The Ultimate Kiss — A Sensual Guide to Oral Lovemaking,* our first question was, "Why?" Why was there a need for yet another *book* on oral sex? There are only two kinds of books generally available dealing with this most intimate interpersonal act of love. One type is the deadly dull, dry-as-dust scientific tome which usually examines the phenomenon of oral sex not from a physical standpoint but from a psychological one. These books do not address themselves directly to the pleasure derived from contact of the soft and moist mucous membranes of the lips and tongue with the genitals of a sex partner. Because they are psychological in scope, these books are read most often by professionally trained people, and so the information they contain is not disseminated to the many ordinary men and women everywhere who practice the art of genital kissing.

The second type is the tasteless, sensational, shoddy, hastily thrown-together popular work on genital sex, usually done by a writer who knows little or nothing of the subject, and who merely copies or rewrites material originated by others — or else makes it up out of whole cloth. The value of such books is limited to the sexual arousal of the people who read them, for they are often filled with misinformation, incorrect statements, and the profoundest kinds of errors.

The Ultimate Kiss — A Sensual Guide to Oral Lovemaking was conceived and completed with the idea of filling the gap left between these two types of publications. We have spent our adult lifetimes studying and practicing oral sex and we modestly consider ourselves among the most expert of the few couples currently writing books dealing with sexual subject-matter drawn from their own experiences. This is not by any means to put down the many eminent professors and doctors of medicine, philosophy and psychology, from Havelock Ellis and Wilhelm Stekel to Eustace Chesser, Frank S. Caprio, and Masters/Johnson, who have written studies on the subject. Our approach is different. We have been able to find only a handful of books that treat the topic of oral sex from the standpoint of *delight* — that it is a sexual experience which is extremely pleasurable to those involved; that they seek it again and again *because* is it pleasurable. And they seek this pleasure knowing full well that it is a noncoital form of sex and does not lead to reproduction — it is, for many men and women, nothing but the purest, most unadulterated form of pleasure.

A few words need to be said at the outset on a matter with no place in the following pages. These few words deal with guilt. It has often been repeated in psychological literature that guilt and the shame that accompanies it are factors which prevent many people from enjoying the fullest forms of sexual expression.

Guilt sometimes inhibits an individual from finding pleasure in things otherwise enjoyable. Our position toward the guilt or hesitation an individual may feel toward performing any of the oral sex acts described in the following pages is simply this: if you are in the slightest degree uncomfortable doing them, then *don't*.

We are not urging anyone to perform sexual acts against his or her wishes. We do not suggest to any reader that because we write about it in an approving manner, and because we approve of it for ourselves and enjoy each other in an oral manner quite frequently, that they should do so unless they really desire to. The following pages hold nothing for anyone who does not go along with our views. However, Jacqueline and I share the strong feeling that oral sex practiced in a loving manner between two people can be the highest form of sexual expression.

The reader will note that we do not go into the matter of *homosexual* orality save for a few passing mentions. This does not mean that we condemn or frown upon the practice of homosexuality — which is the normal way of sex for people who are so constituted. It is simply that this book is based primarily on our own sexual experiences, and neither of us is in a position to speak from experience on the subject of homosexuality. Therefore, our book is confined to heterosexual orality — with emphasis on oral sex in the context of marriage or at least a meaningful relationship between a man and woman — not merely a casual encounter.

A man can better judge the degree to which his love partner responds when he is engaged in cunnilingus with her than in any other form of sexual activity because the lips and tongue are the most sensitive receptors of stimuli from the outside. By the same token, a woman is able to anticipate certain needs of her man when she surrounds his penis with a receptive mouth.

The following material has been broken down for ease of presentation into three sections because the techniques involved from a man's point of view and a woman's point of view are vastly different. Part One: "Man to Woman," consists of those methods and techniques a man employs when kissing, licking, or sucking the genitalia of a woman. The first principle is that a man should become extremely familiar with what we call *The Geography of Venus*. He should know the structure of those parts he's kissing.

Without this information a man cannot do the most effective job of providing his partner with the most magnificent sense of pleasure. However, we do not recommend utilization of the kind of photographs or sketches often found in medical books on the subject. These bear about as much relation to the vagina of a real woman as a crudely drawn map does to a particularly beautiful part of the countryside. It is absolutely necessary for a man to make a physical inspection, lovingly and sympathetically, of the genitalia of the woman who is going to accept his lingual caresses.

In the second chapter of Part One, titled "The Basic Love Kiss," we explain the fundamental techniques of cunnilingus as we have developed them through years of experimentation.

These basic techniques are all that a man needs to master to bring his woman to the most ecstatic pleasure possible. But they need to be *learned*. There is no instinct in man that guides him to the proper techniques of cunnilingus. We deal here in detail with such matters as the proper way to lick and suck a woman's clitoris to provide her with the greatest pleasure. I (Steven) also deal with the use of the tongue between the major and minor lips of the woman's genitalia and describe the technique necessary to obtain the maximum penetration of the tongue into the vagina.

Chapter Three of Part One, "Variations on a Lingual Theme," delves into techniques more sophisticated than those described in "The Basic Love Kiss." We explore the use of a variety of sex-toys in conjunction with oral sex to add special fillips to the practice of oral kissing. Also discussed here is the technique of analingus, the application of the tongue to the anus of your sex partner for the purpose of adding to her pleasure.

Part Two is entitled "Woman to Man." In this section Jacqueline has written a detailed account based on her long experience utilizing every technique she has ever learned to bring her husband pleasure with her lips and tongue. The first chapter of Part Two is called "The Shaft of Eros," and like its counterpart in "Man to Woman," it deals with the structure of the penis, with particular attention paid to the most sensitive areas. These areas of sensitivity are not the same for every man, but there are sufficient similarities to make this information vital.

Chapter Two, "The Mouth of Love," deals entirely with the basic techniques of fellatio, what to do to fellate a man to climax. Jacqueline shows clearly that it is not sufficient for a woman simply to form her lips around an erect organ and bob her head up and down over it until the man climaxes if it is her intention to give the most pleasure. Here are described some special techniques for the use of vibrators in conjunction with oral sex and some magnificently exciting techniques where she takes Steven's testicles in her mouth and makes of that a highly erotic act.

Part Three, called "Contemporary Oral Sex," looks at oral-genital sex in ways perhaps never previously examined. The first chapter deals with the great rise in the practice of oral sex in recent years. The most dramatic increase is among the younger population — some of whom, we have discovered, utilize cunnilingus and fellatio as contraceptive methods, while others, probably the more mature in this age group, frankly and openly indulge in oral sex because it is so exquisitely delightful. In the final chapter we round out the book with the case histories of a group of young adults.

In brief outline, then, that's the story of the book that follows. You will find it much more detailed, much more frank, much more honest than any other book on oral sex you have ever read. It is our sincere wish that from its pages you may derive the kind of pleasure we have found in putting it together.

Jacqueline and Steven Franklin
Quartz Hill, California

The ULTIMATE KISS

A SENSUAL GUIDE TO ORAL LOVEMAKING

The ULTIMATE KISS

PART ONE

MAN
TO
WOMAN

BY
STEVEN FRANKLIN

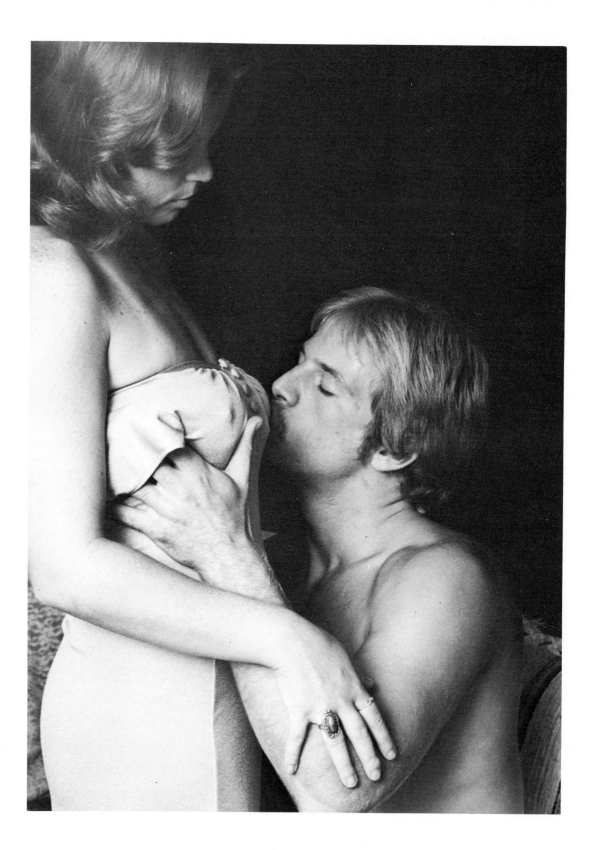

Chapter One
THE GEOGRAPHY OF VENUS

It is a curious fact of human psychology that most men are not particularly stimulated by observing the primary female sexual parts. I am talking about a close and intimate look at the opened lips of a female's genitals, revealing the *labia majora* or large lips, the clitoris, the *labia minora* or small lips, and the opening of the vagina. Most men are instead turned on by secondary sexual characteristics, usually the breasts, the pubic hair, the thighs and legs. However, if you are going to become adept in the art of genital kissing, you must know in intimate detail the parts of the female body with which your lips and tongue are going to come into contact. What we call The Geography of Venus. One of the best ways to do that, if you can approach your partner with a degree of unselfconsciousness, is to examine her body in as near a normal state as possible. With her help, you should identify the following:

a. her vagina
b. her clitoris
c. her meatus
d. her *labia minora*
e. her *labia majora*

The Vagina

Many men are reluctant to look directly at the vagina of a woman almost as if they feared examining too closely the point from which they started life. Yet, the vagina can be, and is for me, one of the most attractive parts of a woman's body. Jacqueline's vagina, that opening in her body designed for the dual purposes of sexual pleasure and childbirth, is a lovely thing. The responses it can produce in her body are fascinating. In its quiescent state, convoluted folds of tissue close the circular opening firmly but offer no resistance to the gentle intrusion of an appropriately shaped object. It is possible in some women actually to see the spasmodic contractions of her orgasm if you are watching for them at the moment they occur.

Many women are relatively insensitive to stimulation around or in the vagina while others have an area (a short distance inside the vaginal canal) of extreme sensitivity. If your partner is sensitive within the vagina and if you can reach those spots of sensitivity (they are located half-an-inch or so inside the vagina at approximately eight and four o'clock), you can indeed produce some of the most delightful sensations your love

Arousal begins for the man with visual appreciation of the woman's breasts, legs, hips and buttocks.

Gradually, the focus of arousal becomes more specific, centering on specific features such as the breasts.

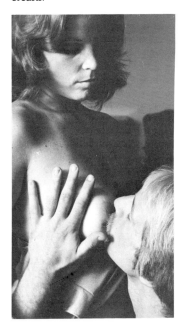

1

The woman shows willingness by opening herself to the man, urging him to touch her body.

She bares her breasts and offers them to his kisses and caresses.

partner will ever experience. Because this kind of penetration with your tongue is difficult, I will reserve details of its practice for a later chapter. It requires some rather sophisticated techniques of genital kissing in order to produce it most efficiently.

The Clitoris

The clitoris rests near the top of the female cleft and is a small, highly sensitive protuberance. For many women the clitoris is the primary source of erotic arousal. It is so highly sensitive that most women cannot endure direct stimulation of it although a gentle, tender licking of the clitoris and the sucking of it can be extremely delightful provided you are aware of the tolerance your partner has for this particular kind of stimulation.

The clitoris is often hooded, the hood consisting of a covering of tissue over the top and sometimes the end or tip of the clitoris. This hood serves the purpose of protecting the nerve-ending-rich tissue of the clitoris from unwanted stimulation. When a woman has a pronounced hood covering, the underside of her clitoris is not protected and will seem extraordinarily sensitive. Many women cannot endure much direct stimulation to this very sensitive part of the clitoris without undergoing sensations so acute they are akin to pain.

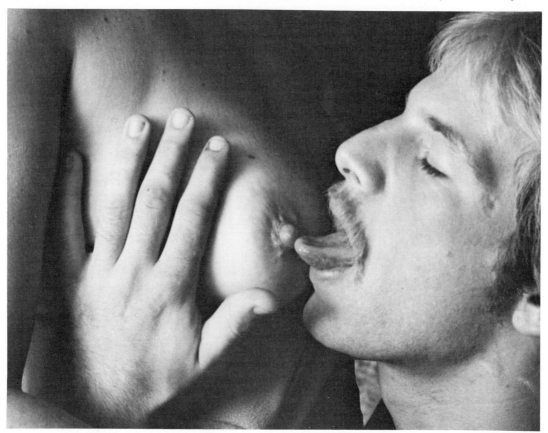

2

Therefore, if at any time your partner tends to pull away from you or wants you to stop clitoral stimulation we urge you to do so at once. Since the clitoris is the primary part of the female genitalia involved in your genital kissing, it is imperative that you learn as much as possible about the effect its stimulation has on the eroticism of your partner.

It is a truism that every woman reacts differently to stimulation of her clitoris, but the obvious nature of this physiological fact is often overlooked. Techniques that are appropriate to one woman, providing her with the most intense sensations, may not only be non-pleasurable but may also be distasteful to another woman. But since the likelihood that most if not all of your oral sex indulgence will be with the sex partner you have chosen for life, then you can become an expert in understanding her particular responses. Your primary aim, when providing your partner with the genital kiss, should always be to make her pleasure as absolutely fantastic as you possibly can. In fact, if that is your aim in all of your sexual activity with her, I can assure you that you will be more than amply rewarded.

The Meatus

Next, you should identify the meatus which is not usually regarded as a sex organ but does play an important role in the oral sex activities of many women. If it should prove that your woman is highly sensitive in this area, you should be familiar with its location and how to stimulate it. The meatus is a tiny opening in the woman's body located below her clitoris and above her vagina. It is the opening through which she urinates, and because it is surrounded with highly sensitive nerve-endings, stimulation of it with your tongue can prove to be highly arousing for her.

Medical literature contains accounts of many women who masturbate by inserting various slender objects within the meatus and during the bodily spasms produced by their orgasm lose these objects and have to have them removed medically. This is sufficient indication of the highly erotic nature of this part of a woman's body. We do not advocate the insertion of any foreign objects into the meatus because of the ever-present danger of infection or of losing them within the body, not to mention the attendant discomfort and pain, as well as the embarrassment of having to have them removed by a doctor.

The Labia Minora

The *labia minora* are the small lips that form a case or shield between the clitoris and vagina. They exist totally within the folds of the outer lips and are not particularly subject to erotic stimulation. In some women they are so small as to be virtually non-existent though careful examination will usually reveal them. Sometimes they are quite large; when this condition exists, they often give the appearance of a rooster's comb.

While it is true that the *labia minora* are not specifically a sex organ, there are some oral techniques utilizing them that can add

Passionate kissing with the lips and tongue is the most usual form of oral sex.

3

The outer lips of the labia are richly endowed with sexually sensitive nerve endings.

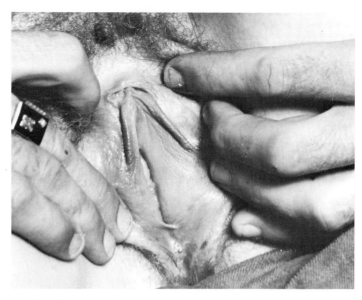

to the pleasure experienced by your love partner. These techniques we will take up in the chapter dealing with the more sophisticated forms of orality.

The Labia Majora

The outer lips, or *labia majora,* close and protect the genitalia of a woman, and when closed, form the slit with which all males are familiar at least from the age of puberty. As in the case of the *labia minora,* the *labia majora* are not usually regarded specifically as a sex organ. However, many women find a high degree of masturbatory pleasure by a gentle tugging and pulling of the large lips. If this pattern has been established by your partner, the sucking of the labia into your mouth with a gentle

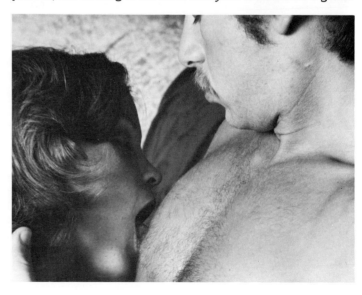

The male nipples are often sexually sensitive to the touch of a woman's lips.

4

tugging motion at the same time can add to her sensations of delight.

If you have a woman who will allow you to examine her genitalia, you will reverse the order listed here. We have discussed these various parts in their order in which you will encounter them when you are in the act of examining a woman's intimate parts.

To make the actual inspection, which is absolutely vital before you proceed with the rest of this book, I suggest you have the woman place herself on her back on a broad, flat surface such as a bed or the floor. Have her place a pillow under her hips to bring her genitals into a more convenient position for your examination. Be sure to be gentle in this examination as well as in all your other activities involving the female's genitalia. The tender mucous membranes are easily subjected to damage.

With your finger gently open the outer lips so that you can see the pinkish, moist inner flesh of her genitals. Locate the small lips that form a beautiful frame for the sensitive areas of your woman's body. Notice how they curve gently from the top of the

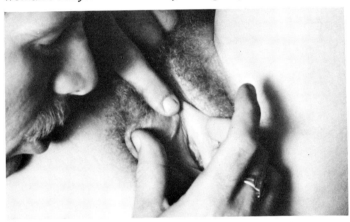

The clitoris is easily stimulated by a light, rolling motion with the fingertip.

Tactile stimulation of the breasts and nipples can continue through all the stages of lovemaking.

cleft in a double ellipse and how, when her legs spread, they fall gently away and leave the clitoris, the meatus, and the vagina unobstructed. Locate the meatus; in that search you may need the help of your partner. Sometimes it's so small and unobtrusive that it is hardly visible. Undoubtedly, you are already familiar with her vagina but it will do you no harm to look closely at its outer structure. It will have convoluted folds of soft, pink and very delicate tissues. During this examination there will undoubtedly be some evidence of her sexual secretions already making themselves manifest from the stimulation of your gaze. Insert a finger into her vagina, and notice how the tissue forms itself to fit snugly in both instances. That is what vaginal tissue does when a penis is inserted, but it is also a phenomenon that occurs when you learn to insert your tongue into her vagina.

Next turn your attention to her clitoris. This marvelous little organ varies greatly in size from woman to woman and has been called a penis-in-miniature by some authorities. It has the capability under the influence of extreme erotic arousal of

5

becoming erect and providing the woman ever greater heights of sexual satisfaction. The clitoris is for most women the single most pleasure-producing part of their bodies. For that reason, it plays a major part in the stimulation a woman receives in all sexual activity and becomes the primary target for the love kiss when you are going to stimulate her with your lips and tongue. When the clitoris is licked gently, particularly on the underside, a woman receives the most direct erotic stimulation she is likely to experience. The same holds true when this tiny organ is sucked tenderly between the lips and given a combination of sucking and licking at the same time.

If you have examined your partner with the kind of care and scrutiny I have suggested, both you and she are probably in a high state of erotic arousal. I am not pedantic enough to think that you are going to wait until you have finished reading this book to put into practice some of the techniques you probably already know. I only ask you to remember that whatever sexual practice you choose to engage in should be mutually desired. As an old philosophy professor of mine used to say, "All love is free love." What he meant, of course, is that if the love isn't freely given, then it isn't love at all.

Allowing a man access to kiss her breasts is one way a woman indicates sexual surrender.

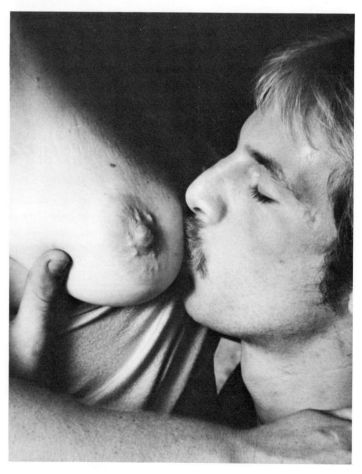

6

As arousal spirals, the man's lips
move toward the vulva but his
hands continue to caress the
nipples.

Chapter Two
THE BASIC LOVE KISS

When a man intends to offer his love partner a genital kiss as a prelude to coitus or a means of providing sufficient orgasms to satisfy for the moment her sexual needs, there are several things he should take into consideration. Some are so elementary they should require no explanation and yet are many times so completely overlooked that they might spoil what could otherwise have been a delightful oral sex encounter.

One of the most common mistakes beardless men make is to approach their partner with a slight stubble. The terribly sensitive mucous membranes that constitute the female genitalia cannot endure the abrasion of beard-stubble for more than a moment without pain. Therefore, it is absolutely essential when providing your partner with a love kiss that you be clean shaven. Of course, a man who wears a beard which has grown out to the point where the hair has become soft does not have this problem, but a man who is normally clean-shaven should be *freshly* shaven before offering his partner a genital kiss.

Next to be considered is proper selection of the place. Any kind of sexual indulgence is, for most women, a very private occupation. That feeling of privacy is all the more important when you are performing cunnilingus. Most people find the bedroom the most convenient place for all their sexual activity, and this room is more than adequate if secure from the sudden and unwanted interruption of a child needing a nocturnal glass of water or the sudden entry of a relative looking for the phone book. Interruptions of these kinds cannot do anything but spoil the warm and sensuous mood that is really an essential part of the emotional preparedness for giving and receiving the genital kiss.

The third preliminary consideration that is of vital importance is the position that you are going to use. While we will talk later about specific positions for specific kinds of genital kisses, there is one primary choice that must be made at the outset. I'm sure you will realize that there are two basic ways you can approach the female genitalia with your lips and tongue. One is from below, and the other is where you approach her from above, your chest resting lightly on her stomach and your lips and tongue finding her genitalia with the top of your head facing in the direction of her feet. This kind of choice may not seem to be of particular significance, but it is vital because the effect your genital kiss will have on your partner will vary depending on which of these approaches you use.

The woman can communicate degrees of pleasure by a varying pressure on the man's head as he performs cunnilingus.

Sexual contact generally begins and
ends with a kiss — the most
universal sex act outside of
masturbation.

So acute are the sensations produced by oral sex that it is difficult to remain dispassionate enough to give oral love with skill while receiving it in return.

Should it be your intention to engage in what the French call *soixante-neuf*, or more commonly in English, "sixty-nine," the simultaneous and mutual kiss (where the man is performing cunnilingus on the woman at the same time she is fellating him) the position of approaching from the top is the only one that is practical. Jacqueline and I do not recommend "sixty-nine" in spite of its popularity in the vernacular speech of the day because it is difficult for a man to perform cunnilingus with anything like the proper degree of intensity when he is at the same time receiving ecstatic sensations from the lips and tongue of his love partner. On the other hand, few women are able to fellate their man and give him the highest degree of pleasure when he is at the same time doing marvelous things

10

While kissing the nipples the man can use his hands to lift the soft underside of the breasts, lightly depress the area around the nipple or lightly squeeze the entire breast.

with his lips and tongue on her clitoris and in her vagina.

The approach from the top can be used to good advantage by the woman manually stimulating her man's erect penis at the same time that he is performing cunnilingus on her. Aside from this possible use, Jacqueline and I long ago discarded this position in favor of the one in which I kneel between her legs and approach her genitalia from the bottom. There are several advantages to this position. I am free to use my lips and tongue on any part of her genitalia without the necessity of changing my position in the slightest. At the same time this position allows me to bring into play my fingers or utilize any of the sophisticated sex-toys we will discuss in a later chapter, on and around her vagina and anus at the same time I am performing the love kiss.

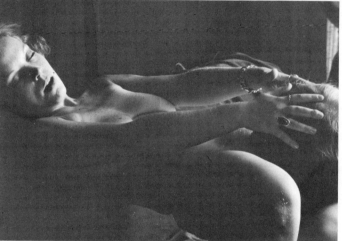

With the woman's legs open and dangling from the bed, the kneeling man is comfortable and has complete access for cunnilingus.

One of the variations of this position we find most satisfactory is for Jacqueline to lie crosswise on the bed, her legs hanging to the floor. I kneel on the floor and bring my face into proximity with her genitalia. In this way I can provide her with genital kisses with a high degree of flexibility in movement and without tension on the back muscles in this position if we are both flat on our bed.

As I have stated earlier, the clitoris is the primary object of the genital kiss for most couples. Since you will spend more time when performing cunnilingus using your lips and tongue to stimulate the clitoris of your partner, it behooves you to learn techniques that can be used for clitoral stimulation. Hopefully you and your partner have the kind of relationship that will allow discussion of your feelings and reactions to the various practices you decide to try. In that way you will ultimately discover those techniques that are most pleasurable for you both, and you will both gain a higher degree of sexual satisfaction than might have otherwise been attained.

I am sure many men believe the simple act of licking a clitoris with the tongue should be quite sufficient to rocket their sex partner into orbit, but this is not often the case. The fact that for many women the clitoris is hooded results in the underside being extraordinarily sensitive. The tip is also *extrasensitive*. Therefore, the simple act of licking becomes somewhat more complicated. You must be aware of the reaction of your partner to the stimulation of specific areas of her clitoris. If you approach her organ from the underside and apply the tip of your moist tongue to the very sensitive region, the stimulation may be more than she finds pleasurable. The same holds true for the licking of the tip of the clitoris if she is especially sensitive there. I would suggest that you begin your lingual caresses by applying the tip of your tongue over the hood at the top of the clitoris and working it gently back and forth while noting her responses.

This kind of lingual caress will stimulate her highly even if it is not the technique that proves ultimately most pleasurable for her. If you have never kissed your partner's genitals before, you will probably find that your continued lingual caresses across the top of her clitoris will be excruciatingly exciting for her and sufficient to move her into a deeply satisfying orgasm.

Using your tongue on the tip of her clitoris can be a rewarding technique if it does not involve discomfort for your partner. The

The man performing cunnilingus should remain aware of the most subtle changes in his partner's responses and pleasure signals.

13

only way you will be able to discover whether it does or not is to try it. Jacqueline and I have found that a combination of gentle licking with a moist tongue, combined with a soft rhythmic tapping done with the tongue pointed so it is firm, produces the best sensation for her. Using the flat of your tongue you can try exciting your partner's clitoris on the underside. If it is not so sensitive that she cannot endure it, you will find this produces within her body higher sensations of ecstatic pleasure than anything else previously done.

Continued arousal of the clitoris in this fashion usually results in orgasm for the woman. When she has achieved release, you will find she often pushes your face away for the intensity of her climax will have been so great that for the moment she cannot endure any further stimulation. This you must expect and not be offended by it. Any further stimulation would more often than not merely interfere with the course of her orgasm.

The object of all this is to discover the techniques of licking and sucking your partner's clitoris that provide her with the greatest degree of pleasure. You can discover a great deal more about your love partner's erotic response to you when you are performing cunnilingus than you can in more conventional penis-in-vagina forms of sex. Learning those things you can do to produce high degrees of sexual pleasure in your partner can only make her delight the greater and enhance her appreciation of you as a sex partner.

Acrobatic positions for cunnilingus are an interesting diversion, but the exertion required to maintain the position can limit the pleasure to be gained.

It is almost impossible to provide deep stimulation to the vaginal tunnel with the tongue. The labial lips and clitoris remain the focus of cunnilingual stimulation.

We now turn to the second most important part of a woman's genitals for cunnilingus. Unlike during coitus the vagina plays no primary part in providing a woman with pleasure from oral sex primarily because few men master the technique of inserting their tongue into the vagina far enough to reach those areas of sensitivity that provide sensations of pleasure. There are several methods to do this; Jacqueline and I have found that for the most part the positions required are so athletic that they are worth pursuing only as a matter of possible variation, rather than as a basic cunnilingual technique. The simplest way to accomplish this insertion is to have the woman lie with her back arched sharply on the bed so that her body is very nearly in the position wrestlers call the "Boston Crab." If you stand on the floor, she will present her genitalia to you so that you can achieve the deepest penetration possible. Stimulation of the vagina with your tongue in this manner can be an extremely pleasurable thing for the woman provided she has developed the areas of sensitivity within her vagina that are most responsive to stimulation.

These areas occur at the point where the pubococcygeous muscle attaches at the bottom of the vagina in order to support it. These points of juncture are rich in nerve-endings, and if the woman has learned to react to them, your lingual stimulation of them can prove more rewarding in many cases than penile. The greatest limitation of this position is that the woman is supporting her entire weight on her shoulders, with her legs in the air, and a considerable strain on her back. In such a position comfort is

15

It is difficult for the man to gain access to the vulva from above. These positions lend themselves more to manual stimulation of the vulva — perhaps as a prelude to cunnilingus.

likely to vanish in the first few seconds, and the pleasure your love partner derives from your lingual caresses will be minimal.

By bending forward, you can slip your tongue into her vagina as deeply as the length of your oral probe permits. If you are fortunate enough to be able to roll your tongue (a genetically controlled ability and not something you can learn to do), you will be able to penetrate more deeply. Whether you can roll your tongue or not, its insertion into her vagina can provide her with superb sensations. Stimulate her vagina in two ways — slide your tongue in and out in imitation of coitus; and also make certain that the tip of your tongue caresses those areas where the pubococcygeous muscle attaches to her vagina. There's nothing in the vagina to indicate where these muscles attach. Your love partner will have to tell you when you've found them.

This is the only position Jacqueline and I have found to reach deep inside her vagina and it requires such an athletic position

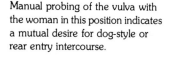

Manual probing of the vulva with the woman in this position indicates a mutual desire for dog-style or rear entry intercourse.

that we only recommend it as an occasional practice since there are so many other ways of using your lips and tongue to bring orgasm. But that is not to say the vagina cannot or should not be stimulated during the employment of any of the techniques of the genital kiss which we discuss here. It is completely understandable, we believe, that the sexual pleasure a woman enjoys should not be restricted to a single form of contact. If your primary purpose is to bring her pleasure through cunnilingus, do not forget the marvelous line in *The Horn Book,* a Victorian "underground" sex book, "A woman is cunt all over."

This quotation is not meant to be derogatory. It is simply a statement that woman, being a highly erotic creature, is sensitive to erotic stimulation over most, if not all, of her body. Therefore, during the time you are performing cunnilingus, whether utilizing her clitoris, her vagina, the *labia majora* or the *labia minora*, other parts of the body can be stimulated manually. In order to provide a woman with sufficient pleasure to make the athleticism worthwhile when you are inserting your tongue in her vagina, you may well be required to provide her with digital stimulation both on her clitoris and on her anus. In the chapter dealing with more sophisticated techniques of performing the genital kiss, I will suggest some of the variations that may be appropriate when you are providing your love partner with lingual stimulation inside her vagina.

Now I will deal briefly with some of the further basic techniques of oral sex not involved in stimulating the clitoris and/or vagina. The meatus, as I explained in "The Geography of Venus," is, when it is considered as a sexual organ at all, primarily stimulated in a masturbatory fashion with the insertion of slender objects although many women find pleasurable the technique which involves the meatus and the *labia minora*. In this technique, performed more conveniently in the approach-from-the-bottom position, the *labia majora* are separated lovingly and the man's tongue is used not primarily on the clitoris or vagina, but in a kind of up-and-down lingual

The tongue is a tickling device. Intimate laughter can lead suddenly to deeper passion.

The light, feathery strokes bestowed by the tongue can be used to caress the entire body.

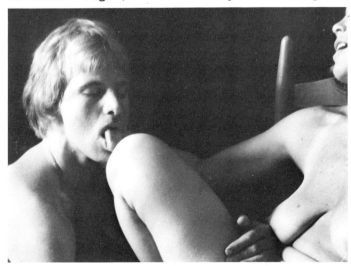

17

The man holds the vulva open to allow his tongue access to the meaty, sexually sensitive flesh within.

caress running from top to bottom through her valley of love. Along the way your tongue will encounter and excite the meatus and *labia minora*. This kind of licking technique can provide orgasm for the woman because at the top of each stroke the clitoris is briefly contacted and aroused and at the bottom of the stroke the sensitive opening of the vagina receives stimulation.

It is possible for a few women to achieve orgasm with the tongue of a man applied only to those areas of her genital tissue between her clitoris and her vagina. I have found it possible to produce orgasm for Jacqueline by using my tongue only in those middle regions, but only under very special circumstances where our degree of emotional arousal, as contrasted to physical arousal, was exceptionally high. It is worthwhile to try to see if you can bring your love partner to orgasm utilizing this technique. If you can, you will gain two advantages. First, you will have added to your arsenal of lingual techniques one further way of amplifying your partner's pleasure. Second, you will have gained knowledge and insight into the depths of her eroticism.

I cannot overemphasize the value of the opportunity when offering your love partner any form of lingual caress to gain knowledge about her reactions which she might never have

18

verbally revealed to you. There is for me nothing more thrilling, for example, than to be involved in a tender and loving session of oral sex with Jacqueline and to feel her body responding to me in such a way that I can sense the pleasure she is experiencing. I derive a great deal of personal pleasure and satisfaction when I feel the responses reach the point that with my lips and tongue I can detect the spasms produced by her climax. Knowing that I bring this about for her in a manner we both find extremely pleasurable is a rewarding experience for me, as it should be for you when you are providing your love partner with erotic stimulation with lips and tongue.

These techniques do not comprise an exhaustive list of the basic techniques which can be employed to provide a woman with pleasure during oral sex for I am sure there are as many variations of cunnilingus as there are cunnilinguists. What I have described are the basic areas of stimulation of a female's genitalia by your lips and tongue in order to provide a starting point for the development of your own techniques. By using the information in this book and combining and recombining these various techniques until you find those methods which best please your partner, you can refine your skill until you are an expert in the art of genital kissing.

The woman becomes dominant in cunnilingus in this position. She presses down upon the man's lips and tongue and rolls her vulva across his lips, his chin and even his nose.

19

Chapter Three
VARIATIONS ON A LINGUAL THEME

The information in the foregoing chapter covered a sufficient number of oral sex techniques to make any man who judiciously applied them an expert in the art of genital kissing. He would be tenderly and lovingly sought after by love partners. But these techniques are merely the basics of cunnilingus and do not constitute by any means every variation of the lingual themes we will explore in *this* chapter. It will not be possible, because of space limitations, to cover every possible variation Jacqueline and I have developed through the years nor would it be possible to discover the vast number of variations loving men and women have worked out between themselves. There are simply too many of them.

What we are attempting to do is simply indicate some of the techniques that we find particularly arousing. We hope by doing so we may point you in the direction of greater lingual pleasure for yourself and your partner. Please note that in this section of the book we are concentrating almost exclusively on the pleasure you, the man, provide your woman. This is not to say that there is not pleasure for a man in performing cunnilingus; many men enjoy lingual caressing their woman and because they do, the woman's pleasure is increased.

In addition to the lingual caresses discussed in this chapter, we are going to describe some sex devices Jacqueline and I use to augment our sexual pleasure. Not everyone is willing to use these devices; some women refuse to use them for what Jacqueline and I consider very strange reasons. One woman we know in Southern California is afraid to use a vibrator for fear it would spoil her for men! Nothing could be farther from the truth especially for a woman as highly sexed as this woman is, but her fear and hesitation are there, nevertheless. We urge everyone to avoid the mistake of rejecting sex devices without first having tried some of them to see if they can increase the fiery bliss of passion. One of Jacqueline's favorite sex-toys — one she carries with her whenever she travels without me — is a minivibrator about four inches long and rather slender. It comes with a penis-replica plastic sleeve that fits over it and is powered by a single AA battery.

There are several ways to use this device when I am performing cunnilingus for Jacqueline. Most often I insert it in her vagina at the same time that I am licking and sucking her clitoris. We have tried several techniques with this vibrator in her

Sex tools such as the vibrator and penis substitute can be used to enhance the sensations produced by cunnilingus.

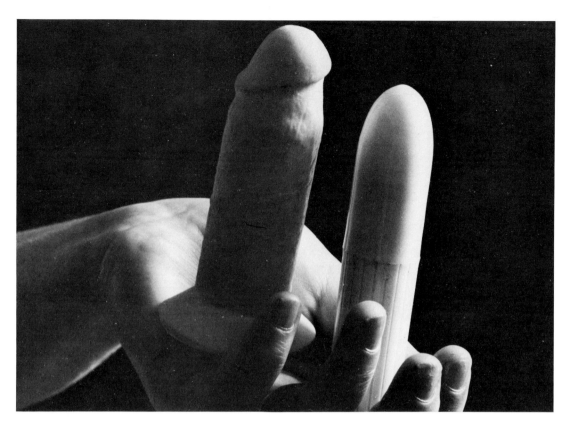

The plastic vibrator (right) is phallic shaped for insertion. The penis substitute (left) may or may not have a vibrating unit installed in the head.

Even lightly touching the buzzing vibrator against the outer lips can create waves of exciting sensation for the woman.

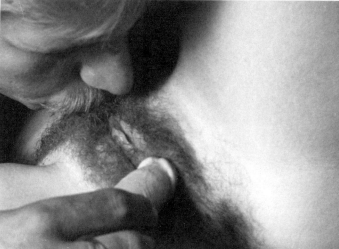

When the woman is well
lubricated, the vibrator can be
inserted into the vagina and thrust in
and out in conjunction with
cunnilingus.

vagina — by imitating the in-and-out motion of coitus (both
long and deeply penetrating strokes as well as short and rapid
strokes) while I am giving her lingual caress. But Jacqueline
most enjoys having the vibrator inserted into her vagina as
deeply as the shield on the hilt of the plastic insert will allow and
letting it remain motionless but turned on, so that she is receiving
dual stimulation — the vibrator in her vagina and my lips and
tongue on her clitoris. In this way her climaxes are usually
overwhelming and deeply rewarding — she often grabs my
hand and my head at the moment of her climax pressing the
vibrator even deeper within her body and my lips tighter against
her clitoris. When her climax is that intense, she often clutches
me tightly for several minutes before finally relaxing and gently
pushing my face away and indicating that she wants the vibrator
removed.

A similar method which some women enjoy is to insert a
small vibrator in the anus. For women who are anally erotic, the

22

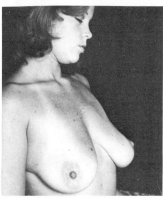

A woman can use a vibrator by herself to create a high level of arousal very quickly or bring on an orgasm if left highly aroused but unsatisfied.

The most exquisite sensation is produced by using the vibrator as a thrusting penis simultaneously with cunnilingus.

slipping of the vibrator into the anus during cunnilingus is exciting and gratifying. This kind of insertion should not come as a surprise to your love partner for the accepting of a vibrator or any other kind of sex aid within the anus requires the utmost cooperation. And it should go without saying that the surface of the vibrator should be properly lubricated with K-Y jelly or one of the many perfumed lubricants sold specifically for use in sexual practices. By employing the vibrator in the anus of your partner and your lips and tongue on her clitoris, you can offer her yet another method of stimulation.

A second vibrator is sometimes used in the woman's vagina, and I have been told that oral sex performed under these conditions is intensely exciting for the woman filling her with some of the greatest pleasure she can ever know. There is a kind of pulsing sensation which occurs when both vibrators are turned on and which may come from the two vibrators periodically dropping into perfect phase with each other since the motors would not always be rotating at exactly the same speed. They would constantly be going in and out of phase with each other; it is this that produces the pulsing sensation experienced by women who have tried two vibrators at once. Add to that the man's gently nursing on the protruding tip of her clitoris and you have an oral sex technique producing pleasure at fantastically high levels.

There are, of course, other sex-toys to play with in much the same way as the vibrator although the likelihood is that they will not produce the same high degree of delight. But many women find this pleasure too intense to be endured on a regular basis and certainly not something to be desired nightly.

Penis replicas, known in the vernacular as dildos, godemickes, etc., can be used to stimulate the woman's vagina

23

The vibrator is capable of producing many sensations. It can tickle, tease or create overwhelming pleasure.

at the same time you are performing cunnilingus on her. The best-made of these devices closely resemble a penis both in size and configuration, and when they are used in conjunction with cunnilingus, they produce in the woman sensations of receiving lingual caresses at the same time she is enjoying intercourse. The method of cunnilingus employed at this point depends on what you have discovered is the most exciting for your woman. How you choose to manipulate the penis replica is also something that depends on *her* preference. Some women find great satisfaction from merely feeling their vaginas filled without any motion of the dildo at all. Others want the kind of provocation they receive from the in-and-out coital type motion of the penis replica while you are applying the genital kiss. Because the penis replicas come in a variety of lengths and diameters, some care should be exercised by the two of you in the selection of the

In many people the anus is endowed with sexually sensitive nerves.

Absolute cleanliness is vital if both parties are to feel comfortable about anal orality.

particular instrument you are going to use to maximize the pleasure your love partner will receive.

It is appropriate at this point to note that there are other areas of the female body quite sensitive to lingual caresses. While the subject-matter of this book is rather sharply limited to the genital kiss, consideration should always be given during sex to other lingual contact that leads to the arousal of your partner and a high degree of erotic pleasure. For these reasons I include the fact, well known by every man by the time he reaches puberty, that the woman's nipples and the shields (or areoles) which surround them are extremely sensitive, and you can furnish great delight by the application of lips and tongue to these areas.

Another area that lends itself to lingual stimulation, though it is much less often considered, is the anus. In the vernacular of the street, the application of tongue to the anus is called "rimming," and many women find it extremely pleasurable. There should not be the slightest hesitation on the part of a lover to perform this act for his partner since a prime requisite of any

25

Anal orality is often referred to as "rimming" or analingus.

The vibrator can also be used to heighten pleasurable sensations from the anus.

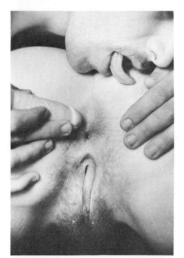

form of sexual indulgence, and most particularly that which involves the genital kiss, should be the most scrupulous cleanliness prior to beginning. "Rimming" is one of the acts best performed with the man approaching the woman from above for this allows better access to the anal region. The anus is an area of the body rich in nerve-endings, and its proximity to the genital regions produces a quasi-genital form of arousal.

In this form of sexual indulgence the tongue is usually pointed in an attempt at penetration. Although it is difficult for any real penetration to occur, the sensations are marvelous. Not every woman will desire such stimulation, nor will every woman who tries it be comfortable with it because of the culturally-conditioned attitudes to which we are all subject in one degree or another. But if you find your love partner is responsive to you in this way, you will have yet one more technique to provide her deep-seated and gratifying pleasure.

Most of the material in this book concerns those oral sex techniques that can be practiced between one man and one woman. However, because we are dealing with some of the more sophisticated procedures, I am going to take a moment to tell you of a particularly pleasure-filled technique for some women. Many will not choose to put themselves in this circumstance, or if they secretly desire it, will not have the opportunity to do so. This technique is simply for the woman, who is open to this experience, to find herself the object of attention from *two* skilled and sophisticated men at the same time. One of the men can be performing cunnilingus on her, utilizing any of the techniques that are appropriate, while the other stimulates her breasts by gentle licking and sucking and by kissing her while she is receiving lingual stimulation. Most

In group sex activities, one man caresses her breasts, another performs cunnilingus upon her while she fellates one of the men.

highly-sexed women are able to last longer in a sexual situation, oral sex plays a large part, but usually is not the entire bill of fare. Most often the men trade about performing oral sex on the woman until she has had a number of orgasms, and then one or the other performs coitus with her, and the other is either fellated to climax or enjoys intercourse with her as well.

Group activity of this sort requires considerably more forethought and planning than any form of sexual encounter between a man and a woman by themselves. The introduction of a person, in our society, conditioned as it is to one-on-one sex, takes considerable planning in order to execute it properly. It should go without saying that such group activity requires a considerably longer period of time than one-on-one sex activity whether the genital kiss is to be part of it or not.

Because of the high degree of interest in the act known as "sixty-nine," I am going to take a few moments here to describe it and some of its variations. Although I repeat, I do not

Soixante-neuf is a very ancient form
of sexual activity.

recommend sixty-nine as a technique to be employed other
than perhaps as a means to satisfy your curiosity about it. Sixty-
nine consists of the mutual sucking of the genitals which means
that your partner is performing fellatio on you and at the same
time you are performing cunnilingus on her.

The position most often employed has two variations. One
has the woman on her back, her knees raised and spread, with
the man above her, positioned in such a way that he can bring
his face directly opposite her genitalia and by lowering it bring
his lips and tongue in contact with her clitoris, her vagina, and
the other Good Parts that are to receive lingual stimulation. At
the same time the woman is able to grasp the man's erect penis,
take it in her mouth, and perform fellatio on it. We will go into the
details of this act in Part Two which was written by Jacqueline,
the most expert fellatrix in the world.

The other variation of this position is for the man to lie on his
back with the woman straddling him; her genitalia are at his
face-level and she lowers her hips to bring them in contact with
his lips and tongue, once again being in position to grasp his
penis and take it in her mouth. There are other positions in which
sixty-nine *can* be performed — side-to-side, for example, with
the woman required to keep one leg in the air while her partner
cradles his head on the inner part of her thigh and thus is able to

28

Frequently, couples who attempt soixante-neuf use it as a means of foreplay for a short time and return to more usual positions for culmination.

perform cunnilingus on her while at the same time thrusting his hips forward so she may reach his penis with her mouth.

Jacqueline and I are quite emphatic in our dislike for sixty-nine and we are totally at a loss to understand its popularity in the sexual parlance that has existed since the first sniggering, off-color remark was made about sex many centuries ago. Granted it is a practice of great antiquity — the interest in it in ancient times is reflected on the walls of the temple at Kahjuarjo in India where there are many bas-reliefs depicting couples performing sixty-nine. The fact that it is an ancient practice and one that generates widespread interest even today does not in our minds make it as pleasurable as the amount of publicity it has received might lead one to believe. We feel that a man cannot do a proper job of applying love kisses to his woman's genitalia while she is sucking his penis to an impending climax; the same holds true for the woman. There is no way in the world she can fellate a man with anything like the remarkable technique necessary to provide him with the greatest sensations in the world when her body is at that moment sending signals that she is receiving the very kind of pleasure she craves the most.

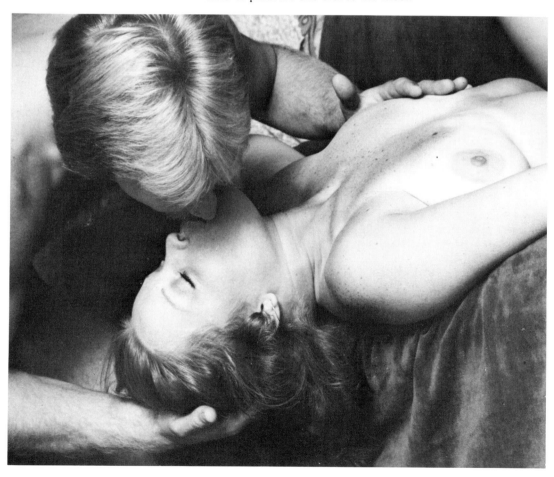

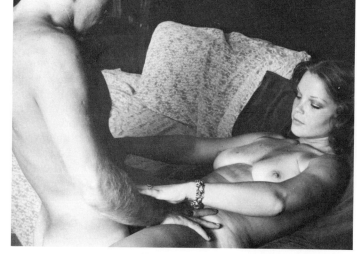

A woman appreciates a man who can give her many orgasms through cunnilingus before seeking his own pleasure through intercourse.

It is our recommendation, if it is your intention to engage in oral sex with your love partner to the exclusion of any other form of climax-producing behavior at a given session, that you perform cunnilingus on the woman, providing her with as many climaxes as she is able to accept or desires before accepting her lingual caresses in his turn. It might be thought that there is in this gentleman-going-first procedure a kind of latter-day chivalry, but nothing could be farther from the truth. My recommendation in this matter is purely practical, relying on the woman's capability of multiple orgasms and ability to remain in action longer than the man. And so she is able to fellate her man to climax most satisfactorily, even after having had her own pleasure from his lips and tongue. The man, whose climax is as intense as it can be in this form of sex, may well be unable to do more than lie breathless for many minutes after his climax thereby making it a frustrating experience for his love partner if she needs further attention from him. Because of the intensity of

After ejaculation, the male is temporarily impotent, while the female is capable of serial orgasms ended only by the dictates of fatigue.

the sensations produced by oral sex (which are incidentally much more intense than those produced by most other forms of climax-producing behavior), the man who may in the coital situation be capable of two or three orgasms during a single session (with a minimal amount of rest in between) will find that he is so thoroughly exhausted after receiving a single climax brought about by the lips and tongue of his woman that he will be unable to perform further. It is for this reason that we make our recommendation for the man to go first in the mutual love kiss situation, otherwise, the woman may wind up with nothing more than a lick and a promise.

We have suggested that the genital kiss can be either part of the preliminary stages of the sex act or as the primary means of achieving orgasm for the woman. There should be, however, no reason other than psychological which would prevent a man from performing cunnilingus on his wife *following* coitus if she finds herself with unresolved tensions or needing further

Some men refuse to perform cunnilingus after intercourse because of disgust at the thought of consuming their own semen. Psychiatrists claim this illogical feeling is actually a fear of homosexuality.

orgasmic release. Many men, I am sure, hesitate at performing cunnilingus on a woman after intercourse. There seems to be a reluctance inbred in our culture that makes a man unwilling to take semen in his mouth — even his own. Psychologists attribute this hesitation to fear of some kind of homosexual taint. There is surely nothing that could be interpreted as homosexual about a man's encountering semen when performing cunnilingus with the woman with whom he himself has just had intercourse.

Jacqueline and I encountered a man at a lecture we gave who objected to the possibility of his taking his own semen into his mouth. His reason was that semen in a man's mouth was, and I quote, "unnatural." I asked him directly if his wife ever fellated him, and if she did, did she in fact accept his semen into her mouth. He agreed that she did but with the perverted logic which accompanies issues that are emotionally highly charged he claimed that for *her* to take semen into her mouth was

31

natural while it would be unnatural for *him* to do so.

With his view we are in total disagreement. But it must be understood that I am not suggesting that a man should fellate another man to climax though I am at the same time one of the most ardent champions of the right of human beings to do exactly what they want. Our subject here is the performance of cunnilingus on a woman immediately after coitus in order to bring her the further climaxes she may still desire. I recommend you do so if you can overcome any reluctance you may have for the acceptance of semen on your lips and tongue because it is one further way you can provide your partner with a high degree of pleasure. And in the aftermath of spent passion you will both find a deep and abiding sense of being loved.

Many women find themselves needing further stimulation after a man has ejaculated. Untold thousands of them each night wait until their man is asleep and then masturbate to achieve the release their bodies crave. How much better for both if the man were sensitive enough to understand the woman's need and be able to provide it for her through genital kissing! He would be repaid thousandfold, I am sure.

There is one factor little understood in the whole area of oral sex. Although it has been discussed by authorities from time to time, not one of them has ever come to grips with the subject. I do not pretend to be doing so here but emphatically state that a man who is willingly and lovingly performing oral sex with his love partner will find a high degree of pleasure for *himself*. What

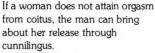

If a woman does not attain orgasm from coitus, the man can bring about her release through cunnilingus.

Another form of oral sex is the tongue bath. It descends the length of the woman's body to the inner thighs and finally the clitoris.

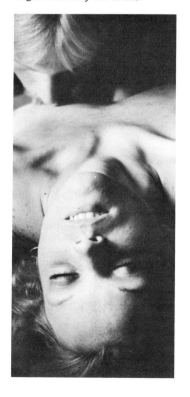

the psychological mechanism is I am not sure, but as an ardent practitioner of *every* form of oral sex that produces pleasure for Jacqueline, I can state without hesitation that doing so produces a high degree of sexual arousal for *me* as well.

The arousal produced for a man in the cunnilingual situation increases his own pleasure if later his partner turns to fellate him or if they join their bodies lovingly together in a total sexual embrace. I find that my own level of arousal matches Jacqueline's, and so the greater the degree of delight I produce within her body, the greater my own. This is only one of the many reasons we will discover in the course of this book for a man's becoming an expert in the act of cunnilingus. The more sophisticated techniques you use, the greater pleasure for yourself.

One of the techniques of oral stimulation that Jacqueline frequently enjoys is one that combines my lingual stimulation of her body with the multiple use of my hand to increase her pleasure. Since Jacqueline is extremely sensitive on and around her clitoris, the technique we apply consists of the following; I will suck her clitoris gently between my lips, much as a baby might nurse a nipple, and maintain a gentle suction. The suction applied in this manner must not be too extreme or discomfort (even pain) may be the result. A gentle suction combined with an easy side-to-side motion of my head (moving different areas of my lips in contact with her clitoris) brings Jacqueline to orgasm rather quickly. While I am performing cunnilingus in this manner, I make digital insertion first into her vagina and applying the moisture of love I find there, I lubricate her anus.

When there is sufficient lubrication to allow penetration of her anus, I slip one finger there and one finger into her vagina. This must be done gently for by this time a woman will be highly sensitive in the genitalia and therefore, subject to any sudden discomfort which may spoil her eroticism for the moment.

This threefold stimulation provides such intense feelings of pleasure for Jacqueline that it usually is only a moment after insertion until she climaxes rather violently. I should point out, however, that many women do not respond in a sexual manner when the anus is utilized; therefore, this technique, instead of being an exciting and rewarding one for such a woman, would be a turn-off. Be certain prior to attempting it that your love partner is receptive to the idea. This is most true if you have not previously attempted any form of anal stimulation. If you mutually agree to attempt this technique, be especially gentle as you approach her anus for she will probably be tense and therefore subject to discomfort. Gentleness in all areas of sex is a primary requirement for a man and never more profoundly so than when using techniques such as this one.

There is a technique for performing cunnilingus that Jacqueline taught me a while ago, and I treasure it, particularly because she was able to anticipate her own needs in such a way that she could tell me what I should do to provide her with a high degree of pleasure prior to our ever having tried it. It does require that you know your love partner's sexual responses quite well and that you do not plunge ahead to bring her to climax as immediately as possible. It works like this:

You begin performing cunnilingus on her using whatever technique she finds most pleasurable. It should be a method that allows both of you to be in a comfortable position for this technique is going to take somewhat longer than most. You begin performing cunnilingus on her and bring her to the point just below climax. That is a point you must be able to recognize, and you will only be able to recognize it if you are extremely familiar with her reactions for the chances are that she will never be able to summon discipline enough to say so at that crucial moment. For this technique to work, however, you must reach the point just on the verge of orgasm.

When you've reached this point, you stop stimulating her body completely, remove your lips and tongue a short distance from her genitalia, and plunge her abruptly into deprivation of orgasm. I suggest at this point that you count at a medium speed to 50. This counting is only a device for helping you to judge the time interval between the time you stop stimulating her (and let her body subside slightly away from the impending climax) and your beginning of stimulation once more. Once again you bring her body to that point just below climax and once again stop.

This time count at about the same speed to 25, and once again begin your stimulation. Once more bring her body to the point of impending explosion; then stop again. This time count to 15. Repeat this action one more time. She will probably climax at the first touch of your tongue on her body, but her climax will have such force and such intensity that she will have

A man can explore the vulva with his hands, noticing the pleasure points by the woman's response and concentrating there during cunnilingus.

Long tongue strokes up and down
the lips, lightly brushing the clitoris
at the top of each stroke are
extremely exciting.

The vulva can be stroked by the fingers and palm of the hand as the mouth is busy searching out other erogenous areas of her skin.

The vulva is the focal point of body kissing. Kisses descend toward it from the throat and breasts or upward to it from the calves and thighs.

never experienced anything so filled with delight; anything that sends such throbbing waves of pleasure throughout her body perhaps even rippling the soles of her feet! Each time you bring her *almost* to climax while still denying her the ultimate release you raise the force of the climax she will ultimately enjoy. Usually this procedure can be repeated not more than four or perhaps five times before it takes only a touch to rocket her into the realms of climactic bliss. Your partner should understand what you are trying to do for if she does not when you stop and remove stimulation from her body that first time, her frustration may express itself in the form of anger and you might well find the session over and any pleasure you are to attain that night will have to be self-induced.

There is another technique of cunnilingus which Jacqueline and I have worked out between us so fabulous I have saved it for last in order to inspire you to try this method at your earliest opportunity. You should place yourself between your love partner's outspread legs and you should have equipped yourself with one of the many types of small vibrators that are available. The technique is to apply your tongue to the tip or underside of her clitoris and then place the vibrator against the underside of your tongue and turn it on. The vibrations are transmitted through your tongue to caress the terribly sensitive mucous membranes of her clitoris. It will provide her with some ecstatic sensations. I don't know whether I have mentioned it previously or not, but Jacqueline is a multi-orgasmic woman on most occasions. That is, she is able to accept more than one orgasm during the course of any single sexual session except when *this* technique is the one we choose. She tells me that the force of the orgasm she achieves in this way is so great that one is not only enough but a single climax is all she can stand.

This chapter cannot possibly contain *every* sophisticated technique of cunnilingus which I have encountered in my life, for to do so would require an entire volume in itself. If I were to try to include every unusual method I have learned which others have found and reported, I would need a whole bookshelf.

In order to provide better access to the vulva the woman can raise one or both knees and spread them wide.

As the man licks her nipples and breasts she can use her hand to fondle his penis and her clitoris.

A possible position for soixante-neuf begins with the woman lying thusly, legs propped up in open position against the back of the sofa. She takes the penis into her mouth and the man bends forward over her body to lick the vulva.

37

When the vulva is slippery with lubrication, it is exciting to both parties to rub the glans of the penis lightly up and down between the opened lips.

The crease of the inner thighs and the crease between buttocks and upper thigh are often found to be erogenous areas.

A shy woman may not verbalize her desire for cunnilingus. A downward pressure of her arm on his shoulders might signal her wish and guide him as he performs.

However, I believe you can judge for yourself from the material presented here that there are indeed many different paths to mutual delight from lingual stimulation by a man on his partner's body. There should never be any hesitation by either partner in the discussion of those parts of this most intimate of sex acts that you find most pleasurable and also those that you find less than pleasurable. Do not engage in any kind of sexual practice with which you are uncomfortable.

However, if you and your love partner find mutual lingual stimulation to be exciting and rewarding, then the more ways you discover to bring delight to each other's bodies the more exciting and more rewarding your mutual sex life will be. Jacqueline and I have found through the years that our responses to each other have grown, and they have grown in proportion to the knowledge and understanding we have each gained of the other's sexual responses. Because oral sex allows the performing partner to know the passive partner's sexual responses better than any other form of interpersonal behavior, we think it should be a part of every couple's regular sex practice early in their relationship. We strongly urge these forms of sexual indulgence as a means of learning and understanding a great deal more about your partner. There is no greater reward for me or for any man who truly knows and understands his love partner's sexual needs than, after bringing her to climax with cunnilingus, to receive a gentle caress and a remark such as: "That was great, baby!"

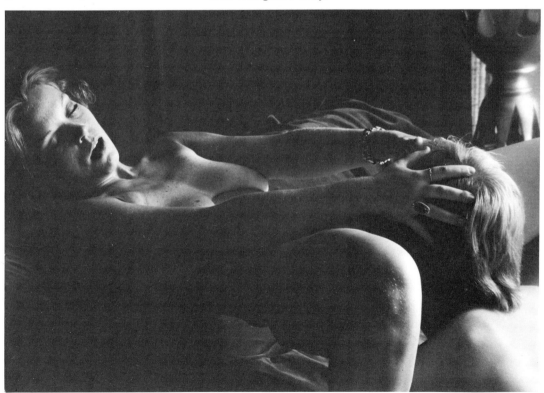

The ULTIMATE KISS

PART TWO

WOMAN TO MAN

BY
JACQUELINE FRANKLIN

Chapter One
THE SHAFT OF EROS

Since I grew up in a household with five brothers, I was naturally curious about male physiology and how it differed from my own. However, my parents were the usual conservative types who were uncomfortable answering specific questions. Once when I was only three or four years old, I asked my mother — in an elevator filled with people, no less — why my brothers did not have to sit down when they used the restroom, and she "Shush!"ed me so quickly and loudly that I understood not to ask again.

It was not until I had nearly graduated from college and was living in an apartment of my own that I discovered what wonderful pleasures the male organ could bring a woman. Like many women of my generation, my first dating experiences included hours of petting and exploring of each others' bodies. This of course included some handling of the penis. Still, it was sexual intercourse that my first serious boyfriend wanted, and that's what he got. Then, after a few weeks, he asked me to fellate him. Though this wasn't my first time (that was in a car with a casual date), now I realized oral sex was at least as much fun as intercourse. And this was even before I discovered cunnilingus!

One man I know, named Harold, a delightful scholarly gentleman from Ohio, once referred to me in a letter as a "cockaholic" after I had explained to him my absolute fascination with the penis and all the marvelous things it can do, not only for its possessor but also for me. If I am a "cockaholic," then I have settled my fixation on only one form of expression, for Steven and I have found a remarkable degree of closeness and comfort as well as fantastically exciting levels of eroticism in our techniques of oral sex.

I want to explain at the beginning of my part of this book that Steven fully knows and understands that he was not the first man in my life as I was not the first woman in his. Some of the incidents I relate are based on experiences with men other than my husband. I believe it a useful thing for a woman to have varied degrees of experience because it will help her understand the differences which exist between men and help her cope with them.

In this chapter I intend to describe to you what in jest I refer to as the "basic penis." I have been surprised in our lectures around the country when I have discussed sexual matters with members of my audience — sometimes with women married 20 years or more — at the degree of ignorance relating to the penis. I am astonished at the number of wives who in the course of their marriages have never *touched* their husband's organ with their hands! And I was mildly surprised at the number of women who had in the course of their marriage

Kisses, caresses and a loving atmosphere pave the way for the initiation of fellatio as well as cunnilingus.

43

Teasing plays a part in fellatio, building anticipation. The penis can be lightly fondled beneath the man's clothing.

refused even to *look* at their husband's penis. On the other hand I was not surprised in the slightest at the number of women over 30 who had never fellated their husbands.

I *was* surprised (because of the great amount of publicity given in recent years to the so-called "Sexual Revolution" and to the promiscuity of youth) at the number of women below 30 years old who had never even considered the possibility of accepting a penis in their mouths. Because Steven and I regard oral sex as the highest form of expression of love that can be exchanged between two people, we hope through this book and our other work to remove the barriers which prevent many women from expressing their love in this way and from receiving a reciprocal kind of lingual caress from their male companions.

One of the first things I am going to urge you to do, therefore, basic to the practice of fellatio (fellatio is a rather technical word for sucking a penis, whether or not the sucking is carried to the

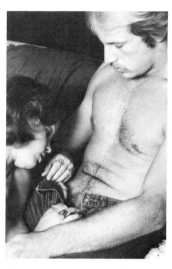

The woman may wish to disrobe the man. His penis may be flaccid when first revealed, but her erotic scrutiny will rapidly create an erection.

point of orgasm) is to *look* at a penis. I do not mean a cursory glance nor do I mean a hurried, surreptitious examination. Instead, I want you to convince your companion that some kind of treat is in store for him provided he will allow you to do with him, and particularly with his penis, exactly as you wish.

Place him flat on his back on your bed, nude, in a well-lighted room. Take his penis in your hand and look at it. He may have will-power enough to remain in a flaccid state but probably not. Few men can keep their penises soft for more than a moment or two when once in a sexual situation with a woman who will be as aroused as you will undoubtedly be when you have arranged to examine his organ in this way. When you first begin to touch him, I don't doubt that his penis will become erect and be in a state where your examination will be meaningful. It must be hard if you are to be able to note the important parts — the parts sensitive to stimulation by your lips and tongue.

The first factor is whether or not he is circumcised.

The most sexually sensitive area of the penis is in the head or glans. The shaft itself is relatively devoid of nerve endings.

Circumcision is not universal in America; there are advantages and disadvantages to penises in both conditions from the standpoint of our providing oral caresses that bring the highest kind of delight to our men. If he has a sheath of skin he can pull forward over the end of his penis, he is uncircumcised. If this sheath of skin is missing, then it has succumbed to the surgeon's knife, and he is circumcised. In either case you will be able to provide him absolutely delightful sensations by giving him "head" — a slang term for fellatio. A girl friend of mine, a reasonably skilled fellatrix in her own right, prefers to call it a "piece of face" — contrasting fellatio and face with coitus and a "piece of ass."

Next notice the shaft of the penis itself. There is a bulbous part of the organ near the outer end, slightly larger in diameter than the shaft, often called the head, but more properly called the *glans penis* — *glans* being Latin for an acorn, which it roughly resembles in shape. The outside perimeter of the *glans penis*, the corona, which joins the head to the shaft contains the many nerve-endings that make this the most sensitive spot on the penis. It is toward this ridge that you will direct most of your attention when you are fellating the man. Follow this ridge around to the underside of the penis and you will notice a point

46

of juncture where the two ends of this irregular circle come together. If your companion is *not* circumcised, this will also be the point where his foreskin (the sheath of skin I mentioned before) is attached. This tiny area is easily the most sensitive spot on his entire body, and it is possible to bring your companion to orgasm simply by gently tapping with the tip of your tongue directly on it.

Pay particular attention to the *glans* and those areas immediately surrounding it. I will have a great deal more to say about it and its role in fellatio. Beneath the glans is the shaft of the penis which in most Caucasians averages between five-and-a-half to six inches long when erect. The shaft of the penis does not contain a great many nerve-endings and does not, therefore, provide the man with any high degree of stimulation when caressed either manually or with your tongue to the exclusion of the *glans penis* itself.

The shaft of the penis does not have sufficient nerve-endings to allow a man to orgasm simply from stimulation of the shaft. In an inexperienced male, touching or fondling of the shaft *may* produce orgasm; the stimulus comes not from the physical contact, but from the force of the mental images that are at work upon him.

Beneath the shaft are the testicles known in the vernacular as balls or jewels as well as by many other names. The testicles are extremely sensitive to pain and are not usually considered

By far the most sensitive spot on the penis is on the underside of the glans where the coronal ridge begins and ends.

Many women find the texture of the penis arousing — a combination of silky softness and rigid hardness.

The woman does not have to
proceed to fellatio precipitously; as
does the man in cunnilingus she can
lead up to it gradually.

The hands are an important part of penile stimulation; she can lightly masturbate him or use feathery touches along the shaft to further excite him.

A popular prelude to engulfing the head is bending the penis against the abdomen and licking upwards from the testicles along the shaft.

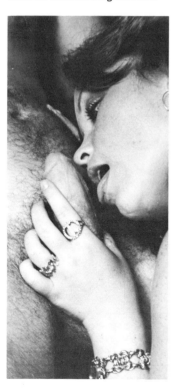

subject to erotic stimulation to any particular degree. However, in the chapter relating to more sophisticated techniques of performing fellatio on your partner, I will detail some very exciting ways you can use your lips and tongue to add a high degree of pleasure for him by lingual caresses of his testicles.

Returning now to the shaft; lengthwise through the penis there is a tube terminating at the *meatus,* the opening in the tip. It is through this tube that semen is ejaculated at the moment of orgasm, and while it is not subject to stimulation in order to bring the man to orgasm more quickly, it does play an important part in certain aspects of your oral caresses of his penis.

Now, without being scientific or too technical, I have identified, and I hope you have identified in actual examination, those parts of the penis which are likely to play an important role in whatever kind of oral sex you choose to engage in with your companion. There are other parts of a man's body which are subject to lingual stimulation that you should be aware of. For example, many men are highly sensitive to the kissing or licking of their nipples, though they are usually not aware of it until some highly-sexed and understanding woman shows them how great stimulation like that can be. The first time I kissed Steven's nipples, he ejaculated from the force of the pleasure I produced for him — coupled with the fact that it was a novel sensation for him.

I have never been able to produce such intense pleasure for him in that manner since but it is still an exciting practice for him.

Many men are not aware of the fact that their nipples are supplied with pleasure producing nerve endings.

I frequently notice that while I am fellating him, he moistens the pads of his thumbs in his mouth and stimulates his own nipples. I have also noted, in other contexts, that his nipples swell slightly and get hard just at the moment of his climax — exactly as mine do.

Another area of stimulation for many men, though not all men, is the anus. Piercing the tight ring of the *sphincter* with the tip of your tongue can give him absolutely great sensations of pleasure though it isn't usually sufficient to bring him to orgasm. It *will* make the entire oral experience great for him, though, and add dimensions it might not otherwise have. Later I will describe some of the specific methods you can use in order to make lingual stimulation of your companion's anal area the very best it can be.

Some men respond to oral stimulation of other parts of their body. A bartender we know in San Francisco goes absolutely wild when he can find a woman willing to kiss, lick, or suck his toes – but in this book Steven and I have decided to limit our studies

Many men enjoy having their testicles fondled; others find that handling of the gonads produces pain.

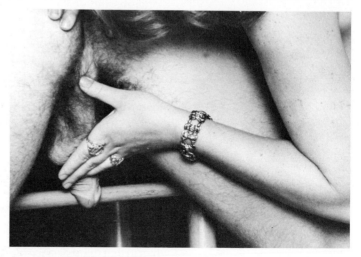

50

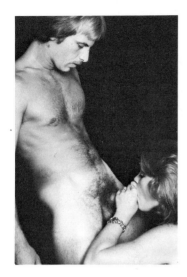

If the penis is not erect it is quite elastic. It can be pulled outward to make the sensitive head more accessible.

A classic position of fellatio has the woman kneeling at the man's feet. Women today frequently reject this position as being subservient.

Teasing positions for fellatio add spice to the sexual act.

to the more directly *genital* forms of oral sex. Otherwise, we'd be plunged into the whole realm of sex activities as well as the entire range of human sexual fantasy — and we would *never* be able to encompass the entire subject.

So study your companion's penis well, learn its areas of special sensitivity completely and be ready to apply your knowledge to his body with your tongue and with your lips when you bend your loving head over his erect penis. Nothing you can do will more clearly show your love for him, and he will certainly return the oral adoration you offer!

Chapter Two
THE MOUTH OF LOVE

It is a sad fact that most women, even those who are willing to perform fellatio on their partners, do not have the slightest idea of how it should be done. Most seem to think that simply by making a cunt of their mouth, closing it around a man's penis, and bobbing their heads juicily up and down until he climaxes, they are automatically experts in giving head.

A woman who offers fellatio to her partner with no more skill involved than that is a true housewife in her bed, as Shakespeare so aptly put it 400 years ago. Consummate skill is required in order to fellate a man and provide him with the highest degree of pleasure possible. It is because there is no source one can turn to in order to learn details of the skills of fellatio that I agreed to write this book with Steven.

When I was first faced with the task of learning to suck a penis to climax, I had nowhere to go and no one to guide me through the labyrinth of techniques that are possible in order to find those that most pleased my companion. I had to learn from experience, and since many of the men I fellated during those first years hardly knew how to appreciate what I'd done for them, they certainly didn't know how to tell me if I'd done a good job. Hopefully this chapter will direct you along the path of greatest pleasure — primarily for your companion, but also for yourself. Even if you do not receive a high degree of stimulation yourself from performing fellatio on your man, you may very well achieve an inner glow of satisfaction from knowing that you have done a difficult job well. There is nothing that should please you more than providing your male companion with the highest kind of pleasure from your lingual stimulation. Every time you slide your lips over his erect penis, your prime concern should be to provide him with the maximum amount of pleasure. What other reason can there be for your denying yourself the supreme pleasure of his penis spurting hot fire deep within your body?

I am further going to assume that you have had the opportunity to examine your companion's penis in detail and you have identified to your own satisfaction the most sensitive part of that delightful organ; you know exactly *where* and *how* tc stimulate his penis the most.

The next step logically would be to offer him some kind of love kiss stemming directly from your examination. In order for you to perceive the most you can about your companion's responses, I am going to suggest a technique that is unusual but highly pleasurable for the man. At the same time this technique allows you to observe his reactions more closely than you might otherwise be able to do.

Merely anticipating lingual stimulation will bring most men rapidly to erection.

Another sensitive area is the taut
skin between the base of the
testicles and the anus.

Pressing the penis flat against his abdomen gives the best possible access to the testicles which can actually be gently sucked into the mouth.

If his nipples are found to be an area of pleasure, the fellatrice can easily caress them during fellatio to increase his sensation.

Lay his penis upward along his stomach (I'm assuming he is flat on his back on a bed, on the floor, or other large flat surface), cup his testicles tenderly in one hand, and using only your tongue, lick softly but carefully along the entire underside of his erect organ. You will, as you continue this stimulation over a period of time, quickly learn those areas that give him the greatest pleasure when your tongue is touching them. Most men respond to exceptional stimulation either by heightened breathing, spasmodic jerks of the body at their moments of highest pleasure or by tightening their muscles, particularly the gluteus maximus, that fleshy muscle on the posterior on which we all sit, or in some other way indicating their pleasure.

When you have found the areas of maximum pleasure for him from your lingual stimulation, concentrate on those areas. You will discover that probably the most sensitive single spot is that point where the ring, or corona, of the head and the foreskin are attached, or were attached before the surgeon snipped it away. By continued licking and tapping this area with your tongue alone, you will be able to bring your companion to climax. I suggest you do this, particularly if it has not been your practice previously to offer him the delights of fellatio, in order to become familiar at first-hand with the nature and degree of his climàx.

54

You should note as he approaches climax the changes that take place in his penis. They will be signs to you of his impending climax *every* time you suck him off and will allow you to prepare for it properly. The head usually swells somewhat larger than it is during the normal course of his erection. He will display a tendency toward sharp, spasmodic forward thrusts of his hips — and most importantly, for most men, there will appear in the meatus (those tiny, lovely lips at the tip) a pearlescent drop or two of lubricating fluid. When this precoital lubrication appears, the man's climax is virtually upon him. Continue your stimulation of his body *but place your fingertips on the base of his penis in such a way that they contact the tube that runs the length of the underside.* This will greatly stimulate his ejaculation.

As his climax comes upon him, a quantity of semen will travel from within his body along this tube and spurt forth from the meatus. It is the ejaculation of semen that constitutes the principal feature of a male's orgasm, and it is the principal difference, as far as oral sex is concerned, between the male and female climax. As the semen shoots forth, you will be able to feel it traveling along his tube a split second before it is spat from the end of his penis onto his belly. When you have produced a climax for him in this manner, your companion will be exhausted, for there is something extremely enervating about an orgasm produced through the agency of the lips and tongue.

The testicles should never be squeezed or handled roughly as the gonads have the capacity to produce pain as well as pleasure.

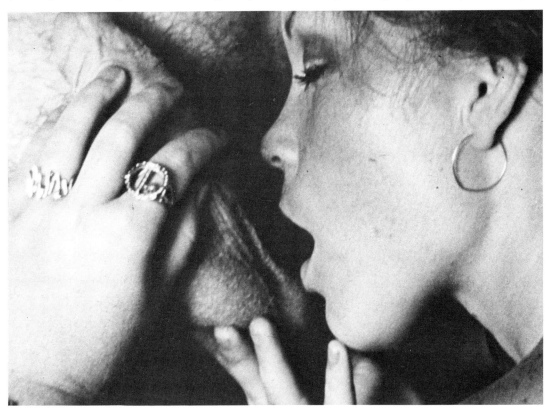

Although the so-called "deep throat" technique is in vogue, its rewards in terms of pleasure are less than the effort required.

After ejaculation the penis will be reddish colored and often sensitive to the touch as it returns to the flaccid state.

A word needs to be said right now about your possible success, and that is the matter of the semen that is ejaculated. When you have produced an orgasm for your companion in the way I have just described, he will be lying there breathless, exhausted, his stomach spattered with the results of your lingual caresses on his penis.

Clean it up!

I think it is necessary whenever you are involved in a sexual encounter to have available an adequate supply of towels simply for practical purposes. This is never more true than when you are going to fellate him in such a way that his ejaculation occurs outside your body. It is my firm belief that the semen resulting from a man's ejaculation is a tender sort of love-offering and should not be rejected by the female receiving it. It is, after all, a part of his body, a part of his expression of his love for you. Therefore, no matter what form of sex you are engaging in with him, the semen is there to be accepted and coped with by you. When you have engaged in sex in which there is ejaculation within your vagina, quite naturally you take care of the semen.

In the same way you should deal with it when you have produced his ejaculation through oral sex. After you provide him with a lingually produced orgasm, a dry towel quickly solves the problem. But some of the techniques I am going to describe result in his climaxing with his penis within your mouth. I urge you to accept this semen in the same way you would accept any love-offering and not reject it. I urge you to swallow it at the moment of his climax. There are many good reasons for this; no bad ones occur to me. The acceptance of his semen in that way

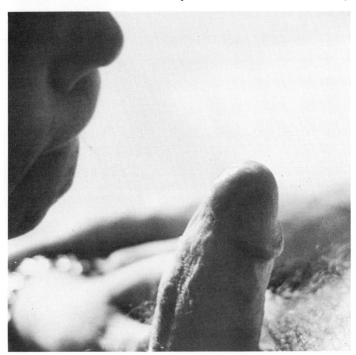

56

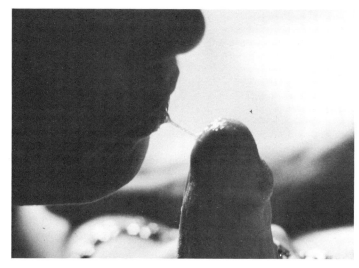

As arousal grows the penis will begin to ooze with pre-coital lubrication.

The erect penis is much like spring steel; a woman must use her hand to direct it during fellatio.

Pre-coital lubrication can be smeared over the head of the penis to create a slick surface that increases sexual excitment when touched.

tells the man just how deeply you love him and how willing you are to accept the physical proof of his passion for you. It is, of course, much neater and handier than any other form of disposal. Certainly the picture of a woman, who has just fellated her man to climax and received his semen within her mouth, suddenly leaping from the bed and racing into the bathroom to spit it out in the sink is one that can surely spoil the high mood of eroticism established.

It is a curious fact that there are still many myths that persist relating to the acceptance of semen in the mouth in spite of the writings of authorities to the contrary and the publicity given

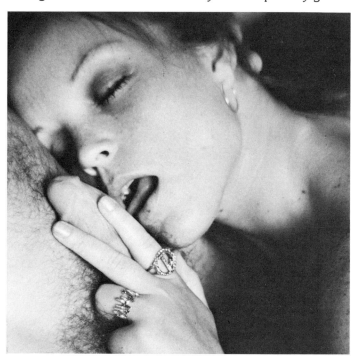

57

them. I am going to mention them though I am sure that even this publication and the many thousands of readers it will have will not lay these myths to rest once and for all.

One of the myths is that you can get pregnant by swallowing semen. This is absolutely false. There is no medical evidence that a woman has ever been impregnated from the act of fellation. Semen does not cause digestive problems either for it is an organic compound quickly broken down by the digestive process. While I have read figures relating to its caloric content, I cannot believe that a woman on even the strictest diet would be violating it by swallowing the semen from her companion's climax.

Another of the myths many people believe is that taking semen into the mouth rots teeth. There is again no medical or scientific evidence to support such a view, but dentists have a high degree of knowledge relating to those substances that *do*

Swallowing semen or pre-coital lubrication is in no way injurious to the health of the woman. Semen is largely protein.

Flattening the penis against the abdomen gives perfect access to the frenulum — the sensitive center of the underside of the head.

produce carious teeth and there is nothing in the semen of a man that would produce such decay. Also, while it is not conclusive evidence of anything, I have been performing fellatio on males of various ages since I became sexually active and my teeth are perfect. I do not have a single cavity nor a single filling, so if we were to judge from my case alone, one would have to conclude that fellatio promotes dental health rather than destroying it.

I have heard it said that a girl who often swallows semen has complexion problems — pimples, acne, blackheads and the rest — but I rather suspect that in the cases where this observation has been made, the complexion problems arose not from the fellatio itself, but from some dietary or hormonal factors.

The licking technique described earlier is a basic method of

58

During fellatio the teeth must be kept away from delicate penile tissues; scraping teeth are the sign of the inexperienced fellatrice.

One measure of male arousal is elevation of the testicles as they withdraw upwards toward the abdomen as climax nears.

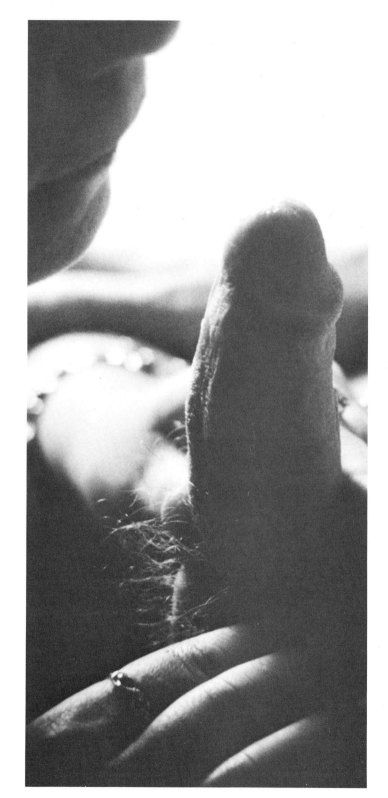

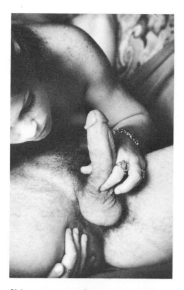

If the woman applies pressure to the protruding veins at the base of the penile shaft, she will see the length of the organ increase about 10%.

This is an awkward position for fellatio as the organ enters the mouth at an angle making interference from the teeth a strong liklihood.

fellatio but it lacks one of the prime ingredients for a successful sex experience for your man. The chances are very great that at the moment of climax, he will have a desire to feel his penis encased or surrounded. This is the case during coitus when his climax is upon him and the instinctive mechanism at work within him drives him to bury his penis as deeply within your body as possible and hold you there tightly while his seed is ejaculated.

In order to provide him with the sensation of having his penis engulfed, and at the same time to give him the ecstasy of your lingual caress, I am going to describe here a technique that is probably the most commonly used method of fellatio in the world. It consists of taking the shaft of the penis in your mouth but not to a particularly great depth. In the next chapter I am going to tell you how to produce orgasms by taking the entire length of a man's penis into your mouth and down your throat — but this is a skill that is not easily acquired, and so we pass it by for the moment and devote our attention to the most effective technique that is also the simplest.

However, before I begin the details of the actual technique, I should point out that there are a couple of things you should know about where you should be in relation to your companion when you are going to fellate him. Because of the structure of the penis, as well as the structure of your mouth, lips, tongue, and teeth, you can provide your companion with a higher degree

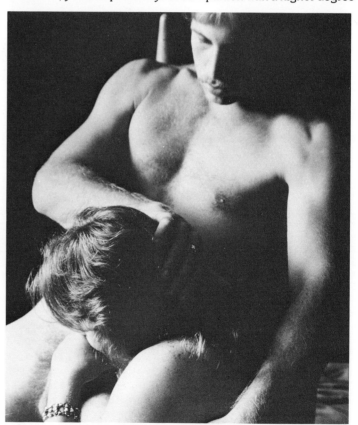

The woman should lie between the man's thighs and bear directly down on the organ to perform fellatio most easily.

If the woman is experienced enough to concentrate on providing dual stimulation, she can caress his breasts or stomach during fellatio.

For a beginner, however, it is best to concentrate on fellatio and let the man use his own hands to further caress his erogenous areas.

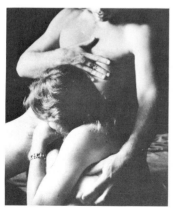

of sensation if you will kneel between his legs and approach his penis from the bottom rather than lying alongside him on the bed and approaching him from the side or the top. If you are in doubt, try the various positions and see which is best for him.

The technique I am going to describe now can be done from any of the positions mentioned but can be done with a higher degree of pleasure for your companion if you are kneeling between his legs. I find one of the best and most convenient ways to do this, both for Steven and myself, is to have him lie on his back with his legs hanging off the edge of the bed. I place a pillow on the floor and kneel on it so I am able to bring my lips and tongue in the best position to provide him with a high degree of erotic pleasure.

Take his penis into your mouth by sliding your moistened tongue lovingly over the head until your lips close around the shaft at the point just behind the corona. Do not simply open your mouth and close it around his organ, but rather give him the pleasurable sensation of having it *slide* in for in this way he will enjoy what you are doing all the more. Now grasp his penis with one hand around the shaft in the same manner as you would if you were going to masturbate him to climax for in part that is what you are going to do. Since the shaft is relatively insensitive to any kind of stimulation, the primary function of your hand is to give him the sensation of having his penis *encased*.

With your lips closed around the shaft immediately behind the head, you have several options, not the least of which is to provide him with a gentle twisting motion of your head from side to side, making sure that your moist lips stay in contact with the coronal ridge. At the same time as you do this, gently work your hand up and down until he ejaculates. Because it is instinctive for a man to thrust as deeply into a woman's body as he can at the moment of ejaculation, you must be aware that he will push his hips forward as his climax washes over him. When he does that, you can control the depth of his penetration into your mouth by the use of your hand on the shaft of his penis. As he thrusts forward, you can raise your hand higher on the shaft still giving him the sensation of deep penetration while at the same time not taking so much of his penis into your mouth as to cause discomfort.

Sometimes a man will be carried away by the force of the sensations you are producing in his body, and will grasp your

The experienced fellatrix soon learns that it is possible to masturbate him with her hand during the buccal caress.

As his climax approaches, she should wrap her hand around the shaft, giving the penis the feeling of being enclosed as within the vagina.

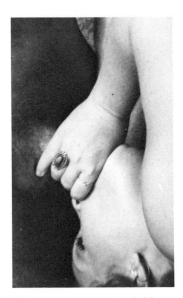

This position is recommended for attempts at taking the penis down the throat.

During deep throat fellatio, the woman can begin swallowing to add more friction and hasten climax.

head trying to force his penis all the way down your throat. It is possible to take a man's penis this way, but in order to do so it is necessary to prepare for it in advance and, in fact, to use some special positions which I will describe in the next chapter. You should be aware, however, that it *is* possible he will grab your head and try to force his penis farther into your mouth so that at the moment his climax occurs you can compensate for his eagerness by pulling your head back while maintaining the head of his penis just within your lips.

As his climax overtakes him, gentle sucking is appropriate. It will intensify his pleasure immensely and increase the force of his orgasm enormously. With just a little experience, you will be able to tell exactly when his climax is approaching for it will exhibit certain characteristic spasms as well as the symptoms described earlier in this chapter. You must be ready for the initial spurt of semen into your mouth; it should not come as a surprise which could cause an involuntary gagging on your part. When he climaxes, you can let him come in your mouth completely without losing a single drop. The quantity of semen will vary even for the same man at different times. But even at its maximum, the quantity will never be too great for you – if you *want* to take it in. I have perfected a technique which allows me to continue sucking throughout Steven's orgasm, at the same time that I swallow his semen. It takes some concentration to be

63

This position is used to bring flaccid penis to erection. Once erect, the penis will be hard to control in this position.

able to do that, but it adds immeasurably to Steven's pleasure and will to your companion's as well.

One of the reasons for the gentle sucking I suggest is that it will help alert you to his impending orgasm so that you may ready yourself to accept his semen and, I hope, swallow it. I should point out that while in the vernacular performing fellatio is called a "blow job," there is nothing more ludicrous than the image of a woman taking an erect penis in her mouth and blowing on it or trying to blow through it. A more accurate phrase is to "suck a man." As long as you understand that

Penises vary in thickness and length; the first position is suitable for shorter organs, the second for longer members.

blowing is *not* in fact the physical act involved, you should encounter no difficulty.

There is one further refinement of this very basic technique of fellatio which I will explain to you with the suggestion that you try it on your companion but only with his prior consent. Without his knowing what you are intending, he can, and likely will, spoil it for you and perhaps even grow angry because what you are going to do will be to delay his climax. Do you recall the tube that runs the length of his penis along the underside? This is the tube through which the semen flows at the moment of ejaculation. If you apply pressure with your thumb at the very base of the penis in such a way as to block this tube so that the semen cannot escape even though he is spasming and going through the entire reflex action of ejaculating semen, and if at the same time you continue to suck vigorously on his penis, you can delay his orgasm for several long moments, producing a higher degree of erotic pleasure for him. His climax will last much longer and be just that much more intense as a result. Every reflex in his body will be straining to expel the semen; it will take great effort on your part to keep pressure on his penis sufficient to retard his ejaculation until you are ready to let it happen.

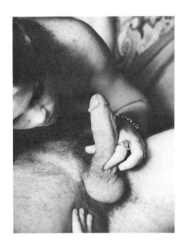

It will only be a few moments before it will be necessary to release the flow of semen, and the force of the shooting will surprise you especially if you have fellated him before and know the usual force of his come. Suck deeply as his semen is ejaculated, grasping at the same time the shaft of his penis, and you will provide him with an orgasm of monumental force. He will be weak, breathless, and completely knocked out of the action for some time to come so I suggest you use this technique only when you've already had yours or when for one reason or another you're not getting any that night.

With the three basic techniques described in this chapter, you can become an expert in the art of genital kissing. But do not go beyond the techniques described here *until* you have become an expert, not only in the techniques themselves, but also in the reading and interpreting of your companion's responses to such a point that you can tell without question exactly what degree of pleasure you are producing in his body. When you have reached that point, then you are ready for subtler, more advanced techniques.

You don't have to follow these instructions slavishly for you will certainly develop variations and refinements of your own — those little things that work well for you and your companion. They will make your penis-sucking as intimate and personal as your handwriting and would enable him to indentify you in the dark among a hundred eager fellatrices.

If you have reached the level of skill described in the foregoing chapter, you're well on your way to becoming what I regard as one of woman's highest possible accomplishments: a skilled fellatrix.

Chapter Three
REFINEMENTS OF THE ORAL ART

One of the first things you will encounter if you are inexperienced in the art of fellatio is the desire on the part of your man to insert his penis all the way inside your mouth. Most men desire full penetration at the moment of climax and are not really satisfied with the techniques of oral and manual stimulation described in the previous chapter. And yet, since the oral cavity of a woman is perhaps a maximum of three to three-and-one-half inches from the lips to the back of her mouth, and the average Caucasian penis when erect is five-and-a-half to six inches long, it would appear to be an impossibility for her to accept the entire length of his penis in her mouth no matter how much she might desire to do so.

However, it *is* possible; some women have in the course of their careers mastered the necessary technique. I suspect that some of the famous fellatrices of history developed this technique to a fine art, for otherwise it is difficult to understand how they have come down to us in history as being the magnificent oral sex artists that they were. I refer to famous women who specialized in the art of oral sex such as Cleopatra. There are also some modern examples that come to mind, but the libel laws being what they are, they cannot be mentioned by name.

In order to perform this technique properly, it will be necessary for you to study certain features of your own anatomy in order to understand the requirements that allow you to take his fully erect penis into your mouth and down your throat.

The primary obstacle to taking the entire penis of your male partner down your throat is the fact that there is a bend of almost 90 degrees behind your tongue leading down into your throat. If this angle can be overcome, then it *is* possible for you to take your companion's penis into your throat — but there are some other things you must do as well.

First, you must be in a position where you can turn your head in such a way that your mouth and throat lie almost in a straight line. I have found the most effective position for this is to lie on a bed in such a way that my head is near the edge with my body sprawled across the bed so my head is tipped sharply back. This position puts my mouth and throat nearly in a line and will allow Steven to approach me in such a way that insertion of his penis can be made so deeply that his pubic hair presses against my lips.

The woman is concentrating her efforts upon the center of highest excitement, the underside of the head.

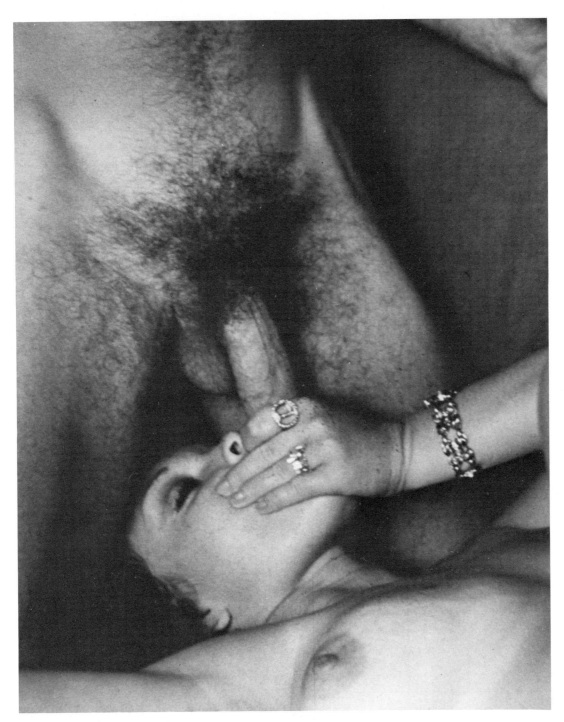

The woman arches her head so her
throat is in line with the penis and feeds
it down her throat like a sword
swallower. It takes practice to
overcome the gag reflex.

This is the best position for deep throat fellatio.

Despite its size, the erect penis can be introduced into the throat.

There are two physical reactions that have to be mastered before this technique can be completely enjoyed. One is the very natural tendency on the part of your body to reject an intruding organ such as an erect penis being thrust down your throat. The normal tendency is to gag, but you can overcome this tendency by the proper relaxation of your throat at the moment insertion is made. You must, of course, maintain this level of relaxation during the entire oral sex experience and because of that it is necessary for the man to generate *all* of the motion.

He must be in a position where his penis is at an appropriate height, and he must approach you at exactly the proper angle, or this technique will not work. After he makes his initial insertion and you have found the most comfortable way to proceed, you will not be in a position to move nor to offer him any greater stimulation than keeping your moist lips tightly encircling his penis and perhaps your tongue pressed firmly against its underside. *He* must initiate and maintain all the motion, but this requirement is more than compensated for by the fact that he can insert his penis as deeply as he desires.

He should now begin his in-and-out motions exactly the same way he would during intercourse. He should start slowly, especially the first few times you use this method of fellatio, so he will not hurt you. He should also be certain not to let himself get carried away in the frantic moments just prior to his climax. He

Irrumation is the act of thrusting the penis in and out of the partner's passive mouth.

must keep the motion in the *same* direction throughout your oral sex for there just isn't any leeway for him to vary the motion from side-to-side.

At the moment of his climax, he *can* thrust his penis all the way inside your oral cavity and that is the single most important advantage to fellating him this way. His penis goes all the way down your throat, and his body will be tightly pressed against your lips as he ejaculates.

Because of the kind of insertion he has made, you will not be faced with the problem of swallowing his semen because the head of his penis will be inside your throat *beyond* the swallowing point. His semen will be shot directly into your throat and thus into your stomach. As I'm sure you can tell, this technique requires a degree of understanding both of what is being attempted and of the possible problems that may arise along the way so that no harm or discomfort will come to either partner.

Not every woman can learn this "deep throat" technique; but the inability to do so does not make her less of a woman. Maintaining the high degree of relaxation of her throat necessary to give the man time to reach orgasm is very difficult, and it sometimes happens in the first stages of practicing this technique that although a woman is able to accept her companion's penis

69

Before a woman will take a penis into her mouth she will want to be familiar with it from observation and touching. Fellatio is seldom performed by a sexually naive woman.

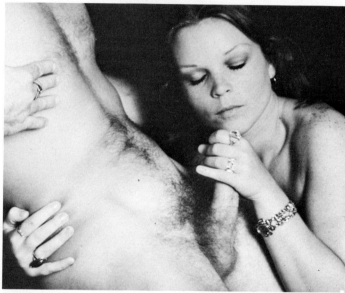

into her throat in this manner, she is unable to maintain the relaxation long enough, and therefore, must pull rather sharply away before her companion's orgasm. This should not be taken as rejection of him, nor as an indication that the technique has no validity in your particular circumstance. Continue practicing for each time you try you will find you'll be able to maintain his penis deep within your throat for a longer period of time. Ultimately you will succeed; there is no question of that for you will surely succeed if you want to!

The only other possible consequence of this technique and it is a remote possibility in any form of oral sex is the danger of an involuntary spasm in your facial muscles resulting in a closing of your teeth on your man's very sensitive and most delightful organ. The chances of this happening are extremely rare and are usually the result of the tiring of the muscles in your jaws — and in this technique we are describing, those of your neck. So there

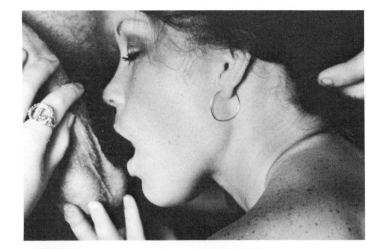

The testicles should not be overlooked as a way to give oral pleasure to a man.

It is almost impossible to achieve deep throat fellatio from above as the angle of the throat becomes an obstruction to success.

If a man expects a woman to repeat oral acts he must show her his loving appreciation.

is the possibility of this involuntary biting but usually you will be aware of its approach. I strongly urge that you do not make contact with his penis under such conditions.

When using the "deep throat" technique, you are not in a position to offer him any other kind of stimulation, and therefore, it is entirely up to him to bring himself to orgasm through the utilization of your body. This is perhaps the only oral sex technique where you are receiving his penis and his semen inside your body and yet you are totally passive.

Mastery of the "deep throat" technique will prove to be one of the most exciting skills you can develop. It will make him value your oral sex experiences together very highly. Because it is an extremely tiring method of performing fellatio on your part and because it produces such an intense level of orgasm on his part, I do not recommend this as a regular method. It is far better to save it for the occasions when you are both in a high state of

71

The testicles can be lightly elevated by her hands or the pubic hair of the scrotum gently pulled.

Many men will instinctively fondle their own testicles during fellatio if the woman does not provide that stimulation.

emotional readiness for whatever oral sex activity you are going to engage in.

Now let us turn to another of the highly specialized oral sex activities which your companion may find extremely delightful but which does not involve the application of your lips and tongue on his penis. I refer to the oral caresses you can apply to his testicles. While his testicles or balls are not commonly considered a part of the primary sex organs (since they are not subject to direct erotic stimulation) when a loving woman takes these jewels of delight in her mouth, applying gentle suction to them, it can produce shooting sparks of delightful fire in her mate.

If your sucking of his testicles is combined with manual stimulation of his penis and perhaps even finger-stimulation of his nipples, then it can become an extraordinarily delightful act for him. I caution you first of all to exercise great care for a man's testicles are extremely susceptible to pain, and he is unlikely to put himself into a position where he can be hurt.

In order to get his balls into your mouth with a minimum of discomfort, lick them first with a well-moistened tongue. This will cause the tiny hairs growing there to lie flat. Pressure on the testicles is one thing to be avoided so it is necessary for you to keep your mouth wide open for as long as you offer this kind of stimulation. Gentle sucking on the testicles while you are manipulating his penis can provide your man with a high degree of pleasure.

Some women consider the flaccid penis to be a challenge to their sexual desirability.

Just as no two vulvas are exactly the same in appearance, the endless variety of penile shapes and sizes is a source of fascination to many women.

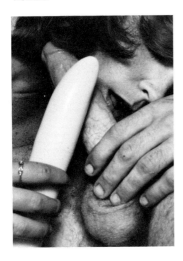

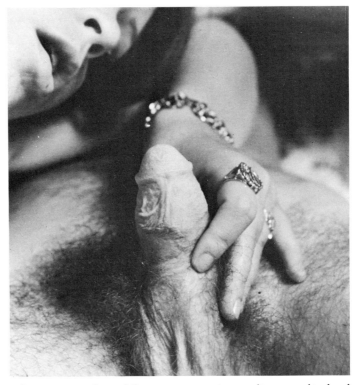

It is a curious fact while many men enjoy analingus and indeed seek it from their partners frequently, they are reluctant to perform it when it is a desired sexual practice on *your* part. This should not deter you from offering your partner analingus (the application of your tongue to the anal opening) because such stimulation can be intensely rewarding for the man you have selected as your sex partner. Since the underlying reason for any and all forms of oral sex is the ultimate, pleasure of your partner as well as your own pleasure, analingus should indeed be a part of your repertoire. Analingus is best performed with the man flat on his back, his legs in the air and his knees near his shoulders. In this way you can bring his buttocks into such a position that they are spread out and you can reach his anus with little difficulty. Whether or not you can actually penetrate the anus with the tip of your tongue is not important. Most men are highly sensitive in this area and the mere touch of your tongue in the region of the anus, with its full complement of nerve-endings, will be quite sufficient. Analingus is not usually sufficient stimulation to produce orgasm in a man by itself. You have, therefore, the necessity of providing him with other forms of stimulation in order to bring about his climax.

However, because analingus is an unusual practice at best and is not common even between couples married many years, touching his anus with your tongue will create highly exciting sensations for him. Combine analingus with rapid stimulation of his penis with your hand, and he will reach the point of climax quicker than you ever imagined!

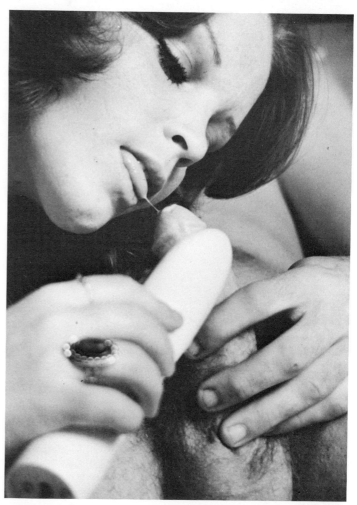

The vibrator applied to the underside of the head of the penis can create excrutiatingly pleasureful sensations.

A man who enjoys analingus will often experience marked delight from the use of the mini-vibrator in his anal region. The mini-vibrator is four inches long and only about five-eighths to three-quarters of an inch in diameter. A penis-shaped plastic sleeve is fitted over it. This plastic sleeve serves two purposes. First, the sleeve changes the nature of the vibrations in such a way that they are more excruciatingly delightful than it would be for the hard plastic to be vibrating against soft and sensitive tissue. Second, since the mini-vibrator is made in two parts, and is separated in the middle in order to insert the battery, it serves also to keep it in one piece during use. Some men, and Steven is one of them, are extremely sensitive in the anal area. In fact he often likes to feel the mini-vibrator in his anus during our sexual encounters.

One of the ways I can produce the highest degree of sensation in Steven is to perform fellatio on him at the same time that I press this vibrator into his anus as far as it will go, holding it there until he reaches climax. The tip of the vibrator just touches his prostate gland, that marvelous little organ through which the

74

The vibrator can be placed along the entire penile shaft to enhance the feelings of fellatio.

Fellatio can be very fatiguing for the woman's face muscles; she should avoid positions which only add to the fatigue.

Masturbating and licking the shaft of the penis is a usual prelude to fellatio.

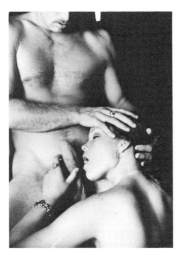

seminal vessels pass. Massage of the prostate by any method produces highly delightful sensations for the man, and the vibrations of the sex-toy against his prostate add immeasurably to Steven's pleasure.

I know of no vibrators that are particularly effective when applied directly to the penis, but this small vibrator used in his anus produces a high degree of eroticism on the part of a man who will accept it in this way. Some men evidently prefer an in-and-out motion with the vibrator when it is inserted in their anus; others do not. It is purely a matter of personal preference and depends on the kind of technique you work out with your companion.

At the moment of climax, because of the sharp, spasmodic contraction of the muscles, there will be a tendency for your partner to force the vibrator from his body. This is not a voluntary reaction on his part but is due entirely to the involuntary nature of his body-functioning at that moment. You should be prepared for that, pressing and holding the vibrator more firmly while he is climaxing.

75

Soixante-neuf is properly
performed with the man on top.
When sensations become exquisite
and overwhelming for one partner
they will often stop performing
while the other continues.

Men like the feel of the female body astride them while fellatio is being performed. This position gives them an opportunity for manual exploration of the woman.

I am going to take a moment to add something further to what Steven said in the first part of this book about "sixty-nine," or the simultaneous licking and sucking of the genitals by two people engaged in oral sex. I agree wholeheartedly with Steven's idea that sixty-nine is not really the most delightful way to receive oral stimulation of your genitals. I think you can see from what I have explained here about some of the techniques of fellatio that there is a great deal on which you must concentrate if you are to do the job of providing your man with oral pleasure with anything like the degree of delight that is possible.

It is difficult to respond to the subtle nuances and changes in his erotic reactions when he is in fact producing highly delightful reactions inside you. So I urge that sixty-nine should be one of the techniques you avoid unless you have already achieved a high degree of confidence in performing it with your companion, or you want to see what it's like out of curiosity. Even if you are quite adept at it, it is my considered opinion that in fact there are much better techniques for achieving the highest form of pleasure from oral sex than *soixante-neuf.*

However, a point I believe Steven overlooked and one that should be noted is the fact that though sixty-nine is not the most enjoyable manner of having oral sex, this does not mean that during those moments when you are fellating him (or when he is performing cunnilingus on you), that some stimulation of the other's body is not only possible but also desirable. It is known that many women achieve a degree of stimulation simply from fellating their partner; but there is nothing detrimental if she wishes either to use a vibrator on herself or give herself a mild

Almost any contact with the woman feels good on the penis, be it her hands, chin, cheek, nipples or breasts.

Twisting the wet lips around the coronal ridge creates peaks of pleasure without the necessity of bobbing the head up and down.

degree of digital stimulation on her clitoris — or if she is in a position that will allow the man to caress her genitalia with his hand and provide her with stimulation in that manner.

The purpose of this stimulation should not be to bring you to orgasm but simply to heighten your responses and to make the session as good as possible for you while you are fellating him. While this stimulation is not directly oral in nature, I mention it here because while the primary act, that of fellatio, is being performed, there is no reason why you should not receive every form of stimulation you can at the same time. Our suggestion of avoiding mutual oral sex lies simply in the fact that the application of lips and tongue to each other's genitalia is so excruciatingly delightful that it would go far beyond your ability to cope with the job in hand while you are receiving this exquisite pleasure.

If you desire to bring your man to orgasm in the quickest possible way, which is sometimes necessary due to the exigencies of time or place, I suggest the following technique. It

is different from any of the more standard techniques of fellatio because it will result in orgasm for your companion within a very short time. It is simplicity itself, really something that any thoughtful woman who fellates her man will soon discover for herself. The technique is simply to place your lips around the head of his penis and provide a kind of *twisting* motion so that the moist mucous membranes on the inner parts of your lips slide wetly around the coronal ridge at the back of the head of his penis. Since this is the area that is of primary sensitivity on a man's penis, this direct, continual stimulation will very rapidly bring him to the point of climax.

This technique does not require any bobbing of the head up and down, nor does it require any particular skill on your part other than to find the point on your companion's penis which is the most sensitive. If you provide the stimulation in the most sensitive zone of his penis, you can be assured of a climax in only moments. This technique also works well to bring a man to erection once he has climaxed. Combine it with a gentle sucking

When a man is warm and relaxed the testicles dangle loosely. When he is frightened or excited or cold they elevate toward the abdomen.

motion of the head periodically to vary the sensations he is receiving and you can restore him to vigor within a very short time.

I think it appropriate at this point to mention one thought that may have crossed your mind — that perhaps there is a reluctance on your part to take his penis into your mouth after you have engaged in sexual intercourse. First of all, you should not hesitate at any time to accept your lover's penis, for as far as Steven and I are concerned, it is a foregone conclusion any time that oral sex is a part of the scene, that the most scrupulous kind of cleanliness will be observed by us, and it should be the same for you and your partner. If this is the case and you have engaged in coitus, the fluids remaining on his penis will consist only of your own secretions and his semen, neither of which

Fellatio properly performed is the fastest way to arouse a man for the second time around. Some women are reluctant to take into their mouths the penis that has just left their vagina.

79

Although the center of feeling is in the head, pleasure can radiate from the shaft into the head.

A man who has just enjoyed a powerful climax may be brought back to erection in a few minutes, but the erection may not last long enough for renewed coitus.

should cause you the slightest hesitation in accepting them into your body — if you are really a devotee of oral sex.

Because the sensations of oral sex are so much higher than those produced by genital intercourse, you can usually fellate your man to erection for a second joining of your bodies if intercourse has been the means of his first orgasm.

Because oral sex is so enervating, bringing him erect a second time by any means is more difficult if in fact you have fellated him to orgasm as the initial form of sexual indulgence.

If you want a second bout, do not hesitate to go down on him and bring him erect for your seconds, but be sure that when you do so, you provide him with sufficient stimulation, not only to maintain his erection once you have turned away from him and opened yourself to accept his penis into your body, but also to provide sufficient impetus to him to carry the act to completion. Remember that many males, if not most, are frequently exhausted by a single orgasm, and if you are able to restore his penis to a state of erection, it will take a great deal more effort for him to achieve a second orgasm. Fellatio performed under these circumstances does not, of course, lead to climax for the male, but still it must be done with that degree of lingual pleasure that will restore his desire. You are doomed to disappointment if you feel the need for more intercourse.

It would be impossible for me to describe every single method and manner of performing fellatio that I have discovered during the years since I first realized the profound pleasure I could derive from this act because for the most part the techniques are simple variations on a theme already established. When you have acquired mastery of the basic techniques described in the previous chapter and have proceeded into the more sophisticated methods given here, you will already be well on your way to developing a style of your own — one which will not be exactly the same as that which I have developed but

80

which will satisfy your partner and yourself much more than a slavish imitation of my techniques could ever do. What I hope I have done in these brief chapters is to provide you with a road map to oral gratification, simply pointing the way for you to the kinds of pleasure that can be yours and your companion's as a result of your mutual oral activities.

The only technique described here which has any element in it requiring close imitation is the deep throat technique. Since each one of us has different bodily characteristics, you may well find that there are differences in technique which you will work out that will be even better than those I have described.

Above all, keep one thing in mind; the purpose, method, and manner of oral sex have just one primary goal — the production of erotic pleasure for you and your partner.

Any position in which the woman can masturbate herself at the same time cunnilingus is being performed is especially arousing.

The ULTIMATE KISS

PART THREE

CONTEMPORARY ORAL SEX

BY
STEVEN & JACQUELINE
FRANKLIN

Chapter One
BEGINNING
TECHNIQUES

In the late 40's and early 50's when Jacqueline and I were younger, there were two words that were considered the ultimate insult if flung at one of our peers. If a boy was called a *cuntlapper,* he became highly incensed because the intent was to suggest that his masculinity was in doubt. If a girl was called a *cocksucker,* she might be quite popular with the boys, but she would at the same time be considered not only promiscuous but perverted in some rare and unique way.

The boys at the school in Berkeley, California, where we both graduated, would be willing to take such a girl out to a movie, preferably a drive-in where the chances of their being seen together would not be great — but she would not be the partner chosen to be taken to one of the school dances.

As a matter of fact, the number of girls accused of sucking cocks was probably far fewer than the number who actually did so, but there is no doubt that many girls actually discovered fellatio as a means by which they could keep their boyfriends from seeking sex elsewhere while at the same time preserving their overly-prized virginity. These were the girls who most often gained the reputation for being cocksuckers in the most pejorative sense. They were unwilling to offer their dates genital intercourse, only fellatio. At that age few boys and fewer girls appreciated the absolute delight that can be had from the expert practice of oral sex. They regarded it as a second-rate method of achieving climax, only slightly above masturbation in desirability, and far below "regular" intercourse.

However, I, Steven, know from my own experience that some younger people at that time were able to engage in various oral sex practices without either ruining their reputation or having their essential sexuality challenged by doing so. The first girl I ever performed cunnilingus on was a lovely, dark-haired girl named Marian, a year behind me in school, who went with me one night in my old Fraser out to Bay Farm Island off Alameda — a favorite spot to park, since it was remote and usually safe from interruption.

We parked near some rusting hulks of World War II destroyers on a lonely stretch of sea-wall where we could hear the gentle lapping of the water against the shore. Marian and I engaged in a mutual groping session, rubbing and feeling each other's genitalia until it became apparent that if I was going to be able to obtain my heart's desire, which was sexual intercourse with that sweet thing, then I was going to have to come up with some form of lubrication more than Marian's taut body was producing.

Coitus is the most instinctive form of sex next to masturbation and most young people begin with manual foreplay leading to intercourse.

85

Young people who have begun to experiment usually stumble into oral sex but are not particularly skillful in their technique.

It takes several near miss experiences with cunnilingus or fellatio before many young people overcome their inhibitions about mouth-genital contact.

I had previously taken the precaution of disengaging the light switch on the door on the right hand side of my Fraser so that when I opened the door the dome-light did not come on. And there, with a light breeze blowing in from the bay, wafting the maritime odors along the shore, I knelt in the gravel and gently spread Marian's legs so I could plunge my tongue into the cleft of genitals to better prepare her for the intercourse I hoped was to follow.

I am sure looking back at this episode that I was inexperienced and quite clumsy, but it had its desired effect. Lovely Marian and I enjoyed what for me at the time was the ultimate form of sexual expression — straight "genital sex." I don't know whether she achieved orgasm as a result of my lingual stimulation of her genitalia or from the coitus we engaged in afterwards for at that time I was as insensitive and unfeeling of my partner's needs as any young man has ever been. I *did* know that performing cunnilingus — a word I didn't even know in those days — had been an experience I found quite pleasurable and which I looked forward to repeating in the future. The many more times Marian urged me to bury my face in her muff were ample testimony to the fact that she too enjoyed it.

The point of this anecdote is that what I was doing was relatively rare compared to the frequency of other forms of sexual expression among the young people with whom I attended school. The rarity of its occurrence was due to not only the supposed social stigma that was attached to oral sex, but also to the fact that genital kissing in those days still carried

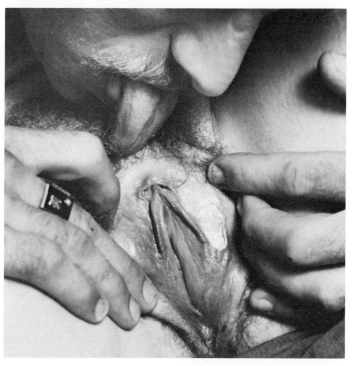

To a less experienced male, oral contact with a bared breast can be as sexually exciting as oral sex to a more sophisticated man.

Women who perform fellatio often use it as a method of avoiding pregnancy.

the aura of *perversion* about it. Furthermore, it was actually against the law. There was very little understanding then — among us young people anyway — of the manifold ways in which sexual pleasure could be achieved. Very few if any of us realized that oral sex was a valid method of bringing each other to orgasm.

Naturally we know today, as do most enlightened people, that there is nothing *new* about oral sex. It has been a part of many civilizations and cultures all over the world since ancient times. But such was the repression of the long Victorian era that "cocksucking" and "cuntlapping" were still dirty words as late as the 1940's. And any serious discussion or evaluation of the "unnatural" oral techniques was unthinkable to us. The topic was simply *verboten* except on a vulgar, sniggering level. The science of sexology was still in its infancy. Even medical men still paid heed to the dire warnings of Krafft-Ebing, the well-meaning pioneer of sex research, who wrote in his *Psychopathia Sexualis* in the 1880's about the "horrible perversion" of oral sex. As a matter of fact, being a youth of literary bent, I had come across an "underground" copy of Krafft-Ebing's book and was sorely puzzled as well as worried over his solemn pronouncements about the evils of offbeat sex.

The puritanical repression of Victorian and Edwardian times, as all know today, comprised a large element of hypocrisy. Oral

87

Even today, the first form of oral sex encountered by most is passionate kissing.

To a young woman, the first sight of the flaccid penis is a curiosity; the erect penis can appear awesome, even menacing.

sex was practiced freely by whores and other promiscuous women and even by a minority of free-thinking "respectable" people — but it simply wasn't *talked* about. We young people in those postwar days had no way of knowing that some advanced sexologists such as Havelock Ellis and Theodor Van de Velde were already moving to break down the barriers, cautiously recommending fellatio and cunnilingus as perfectly valid techniques for married people, nor that Kinsey was already engaged in his monumental research projects that were to reveal how widely oral sex was actually practiced in secret and to lead to belated repeal of the laws forbidding it in many states.

Then, spurred by various factors too complex to go into here, there came the so-called "Sexual Revolution" of the 1960's. The sexual scene will never be the same. Knowledge of sex and the variety of sexual practices is much more widespread today among young people than it was during the years when we, Steven and Jacqueline, were growing up. Regardless of the reasons or of the moral controversies that still go on, young

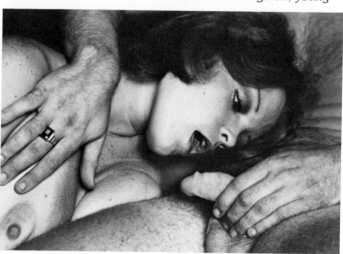

men and women today have a much fuller and richer understanding of their own sexuality than we did. They are more mature at an earlier age. Freed of the hypocritical guilt complexes of former generations as well as being better informed, they are better able to relate to and indulge in sexual practices that diverge from the old standard "missionary position" type of intercourse. In general, the sexual side of their lives as they grow up has become much richer and more rewarding.

Jacqueline's first experience with oral sex was when she fellated her date to climax in the front seat of his car parked in a drive-in movie off Telegraph Avenue. She performed the act, she maintains today, in order to be able to watch the movie! The young man she was out with had no interest in the film but only in Jacqueline's body. She knew that for her to be able to see the show she would have to provide him with some sort of relief to get his mind off sex for a while.

The "sitting on the face" position for cunnilingus gives the woman being sucked control through the downward pressure she exerts.

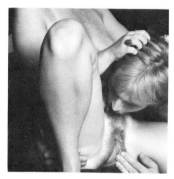

It is an instinctive act during oral sex for the passive partner to guide the performer by pressure on the head.

Breast kissing plus manual caresses of the labia is a usual preliminary act.

She chose fellatio, which she had never practiced before, as being the most convenient of the sexual techniques with which she was even verbally familiar. They were in a coupe, that absurd kind of single-seat automobile manufactured and sold in the United States until after World War II. There was no back seat, and even the front seat was not wide enough to allow a couple to have any kind of sex involving body-on-body without awkward cramping. So she bent over his lap without even requiring that he move away from the steering wheel and sucked him off to climax.

I believe Jacqueline's skill at fellatio is instinctive in spite of her assertion that it must be learned. On the occasion of this first experience, she not only knew that it would satisfy her date, but she also knew enough to swallow his semen when he climaxed.

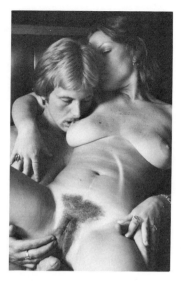

Sliding the head or shaft of the penis across or up and down in the labial groove is exciting for both partners.

Generally the woman does not receive much pleasure from deep throat fellatio. She performs it to prove her sexual dexterity and to please the man she loves.

It is significant, I think, that the young man, called "Senator" by his school buddies, refused to kiss her for the rest of the night – as though his penis in her mouth was somehow contaminating.

It was not until Jacqueline and Steven were dating some two years after this event, that she first experienced the delights of cunnilingus. Jacqueline was quite popular during school; she and Steven did not begin dating until very nearly the time of his graduation. We have been lovers ever since — and man and wife since shortly after our graduation.

In neither of our specific cases, nor in any of those instances with which we are personally familiar from those days, was contraception a factor in the decision leading to genital kissing. Today, many young people (they've told us themselves) use mouth techniques as a means of avoiding pregnancy, as well as for physical gratification. Now that they know it isn't a horrible perversion, they find it more rewarding than masturbating by themselves or by someone else — the traditional method young people have used since time immemorial. The Pill is available today but they may not happen to have any at hand, or for some reason the girl may not want to take one. So they don't hesitate to indulge in oral sex. In our younger days most of us *did* hesitate — even though not for very long in some cases.

90

This position allows for close body contact and kissing as well as deep intromission of the penis into the vagina.

When we were growing up, contraception usually meant use of a condom, either rubber or fishskin, by the male. The most effective contraception method for girls was the use of a diaphragm, but there were very few young women who had been fitted for one. It was necessary for her to have the diaphragm fitted by a physician, and it was almost unheard of for a girl to be so fitted until just before she got married. One mother we knew of, more practical than most, had her daughter fitted with a diaphragm, and the mother was roundly condemned as immoral herself as well as for encouraging her daughter to enter a life of promiscuity.

I find it a curious fact that while young people today have available the oral contraceptive pill to a greater extent than even a few years ago, in many cases instead of using it they turn to oral sex purely as a contraceptive measure. Of course, the young woman who fellates her partner to climax and doesn't allow intercourse can enter marriage technically a virgin, but she may indeed be quit skilled in understanding the effects of certain types of stimuli on an erect penis.

At the same time, many boys who in an earlier generation would have shunned cunnilingus as perverted, dirty, or in some way unworthy of their masculinity now turn to it eagerly. The astounding thing is that the young people with whom we have discussed sexual activity and sex problems in our lectures across the country have displayed a remarkable degree of awareness of the entire scope of genital kissing. Males and females alike demonstrate an awareness of ecstatic pleasure that can be theirs by the application of lips and tongue on the genitalia. Among these young people there is also an awareness of the fact that even bisexuality is not an attitude to be condemned as roundly as it was in earlier times.

It is not uncommon now to find young men experimenting with oral sex among themselves and young women who perform cunnilingus on each other in the absence of a partner of the opposite sex. The majority of those who engage in such offbeat sex-play are not really homosexual; they are merely experimenting, seeking a variety of experiences before settling down into their preferred sex modes. They are able to understand and appreciate that this sort of sexual experience does not make them "queer," and that their sex preferences are not going to become irrevocably fixed by a few homosexual encounters.

There are many girls who have discovered the delights of cunnilingus between each other, who in earlier times would have been subjected to extreme ostracism if their "lesbian" involvement became known. They might have reacted by going overboard into homosexuality or else by avoiding sexual activity of any kind. Young people like these are not depraved, nor are they a threat to the future of society for the chances are that they will eventually marry and establish stable family situations.

And what about oral sex itself between young men and women? What is their basic attitude toward it *today* as opposed to only a few years ago? Surprisingly, while not so long ago,

91

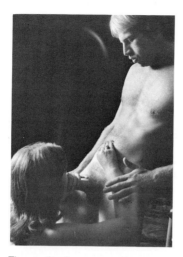

The navel is also an erogenous zone easily stimulated by a woman during fellatio.

In this position the woman can control the depth of penetration of the penis and stimulate herself at the same time.

oral sex (by those brave enough to practice it) was regarded as a more intimate and desirable act than genital coitus itself among young people of the 70's, the tendency seems to be to place it above masturbation on the scale of intimacy but below "straight" intercourse. It is a practice of many young women to allow a boy to "play with" them using only his hands and fingers on their genitals — or else to allow him to go down on them, to perform cunnilingus — but to deny him insertion of his penis in her vagina.

The same scale of values has not always held for the girls in offering something less than intercourse to their love partners. It used to be quite common for a girl to masturbate her boyfriend to orgasm after denying him intercourse; but performing fellatio (sucking the cock) was usually reserved only for very special boyfriends. Even so, it was not performed with regularity, but only as a kind of special treat.

Nowadays, fellatio is much more commonly practiced by those who are seeking sexual pleasure but who are hesitant about the risks involved in intercourse. Even a slight chance of pregnancy, of course, is always a concern, even with an optimum birth control method such as the pill. Not wanting to take on the momentous responsibility of a family has made a lot of those who are not in committed relationships reconsider their sexual practices. It's true that some people approach sexual

92

activity generally, and oral sex in particular, much more casually than was the case in decades gone by. Yet these days most people are choosing their partners with much more care.

We know of one sexually active, but still not very experienced, woman of about 23, named Karen. She was always worried about getting pregnant until her best friend finally spoke to her. "You don't know what you're missing," her friend told her. "Men love it when you suck their penis. And they almost always want to return the favor." It so happens Karen had a date that evening with a new boyfriend. She was sure their relationship was ready to become sexual, and she was right. That night, she tried fellating her young man for the first time. Needless to say, he loved it.

We have heard from many other young women who also limit their sexual activities to oral sex when they are in new relationships. The most significant changes of attitude reflected in these situations is the acceptance of genital kissing not only as an alternate means of achieving orgasm, but an alternative that is quite acceptable and even casual. The pejorative terms *cocksucker* and *cuntlapper* have lost most of the force they had in the days when Jacqueline and Steven were starting their sexual journey through life. Where it was common during our youth for those of us who actually did engage in oral sex with the opposite sex to keep the matter a closely guarded secret,

Pulling outward and down rhythmically on the labial lips exerts a stimulating pressure on the clitoris much like coitus.

A man can tell how aroused a woman is by the amount of lubrication secreted from within the vagina.

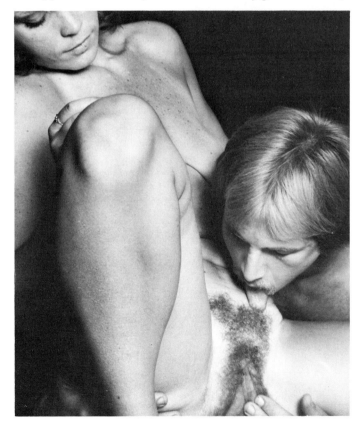

93

today genital kissing techniques are discussed quite openly among young people — even to the point of young women discussing the various levels of oral talent achieved by different youths in their group.

A phenomenon that has arisen in recent years, while it encompasses only a relatively small percentage of young people who are active sexually, but still occurs with sufficient frequency to have some significance here, is the group sex party. Possibly as a result of the publicity given to wifeswapping and "swinging" groups in recent years, some young people have turned to the group sex experience for kicks. One of the most frequently found practices at such a party is the oral sex technique called the "daisy chain."

A daisy chain involves exactly the same techniques as does sixty-nining, and for that reason we don't encourage it even within the framework of the group sex experience. In a daisy chain a woman sucks the penis of a man in her mouth while at the same time another man buries his face in her genitals while a second female performs fellatio on this second young man, and so on. They continue the circle, each person receiving oral sex at the same time as he or she is giving it.

A much more common, still exciting, but certainly safer practice these days is a variation on what has come to be called "cocooning," where the couple parks themselves in front of the television and videocassette recorder with some good take-out food, and settles in for the evening. Now we are not only referring to commercial or cable TV offerings, but rather to the habit many couples have of watching sexually explicit videotapes together.

One couple we know, Rick and Angela, make such evenings a regular part of their relationship. Rick recounted their experience to us this way: "We've been married five years, and sometimes, what with the pressures of our jobs and dealing with pushy in-laws, a leaky roof, and a car that won't always start, Angela and I get a real kick out of setting aside some special time just for us — no outside pressures allowed in. First we spend some time choosing our evening's entertainment at one of the local video outlets. Then we come home, turn out the porch light, turn on the answering machine and snuggle up on

Some women enjoy being perfectly passive during cunnilingus giving themselves up utterly to the sensations produced.

Other women direct the man's every movement and guide the pressure he exerts.

94

the sofa in front of the VCR. Sometimes we watch a general release film first, just to prolong the anticipation.

"As soon as the sexually explicit scenes begin, I find myself reaching for Angela. With my eyes still on the screen, savoring the actions of these fantasy characters, I sense Angela drawing nearer to my penis. Soon her lips envelop me and start moving slowly up and down. If I become too excited by the combination of her attentions and the flickering images on the TV screen, I indicate to her to wait a while before continuing.

"Still, we rarely make it to the end of a video before I can't wait any longer. Once I've exploded with pleasure, we usually watch the rest of the video, and by that time, Angela is more than ready for me to provide her with erotic gratification. In fact, I often try out some new oral sex technique on her, inspired as I am by the video we've just seen."

In addition to the inspirational value, many couples use erotic videos in an educational way, to discover sexual variations they can then incorporate into their erotic repertoires. Listen to Marsha as she describes how she and her partner, Dave, like to

As she licks slowly up the shaft of the penis, the woman can use one finger to caress the coronal ridge and the underside of the head.

As exciting as analingus is to some men, the center of stimulation is still in the head of the penis.

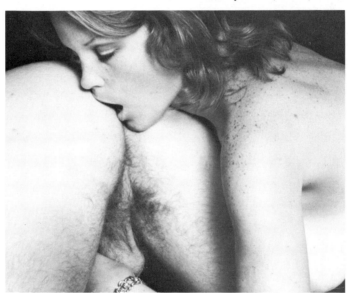

spend their weekend evenings: "Dave and I think of ourselves as oral sex fanatics. Last Friday, for instance, we took an hour to choose a sexually oriented video at a shop just a couple of blocks from our apartment. We went down the aisles, read all the boxes, pointing out interesting ones to each other. It's kind of fun seeing what turns each other on, even at that preliminary level. We finally chose one which featured several couples and which focused mostly on oral techniques.

"When we got home, we started watching right away. Slowly Dave began undressing me, partly watching me, partly watching the screen. Even when he wasn't watching me, his hands were gauging my responsiveness and readiness. Next I leaned over and took his penis into my mouth. Whatever the

95

If a man is anally erotic, fellatio combined with a vibrator at the anal sphincter is an ecstatic sensation.

Many young women are fascinated by the male penis and the effect they can produce on it as it erects.

women on the screen did, we tried to imitate. When they changed positions, so did we. When she used her hands, moving up and down on the shaft, to increase her partner's pleasure, I did the same with my enthusiastic partner. We even tried sixty-nine, but collapsed giggling onto the floor. It was just too much stimulation, what with trying to keep one eye each on the TV at the same time as giving and receiving the most delicious of oral caresses.

"The most fun was when the couple on the screen got into an unusual position, and Dave pushed the pause button so we could take our time copying them. It felt heavenly when Dave licked all around my most sensitive areas, all the while knowing we had to wait for our video-twins to finish before we could do the same."

Another couple shared with us their favorite time to indulge in oral sex: mornings! Here's what Carol told us: "Ethan loves to make love in the morning. We cuddle all night, with his body pressed up against mine, which I just love. Of course, he almost always wakes up with a hard-on, which he prefers to deal with immediately. The problem for me is that I have to get up and get ready for work in a very short time, and I can't have his cum dripping out of me the rest of the day. It's distracting to say the least. One morning early in our marriage, I simply moved his hands out of the way and began fellating him. He smiled, lay back, and had a great time. I got aroused myself, of course, especially when it was obvious my first task of the day was nearing a satisfactory completion. Still, I like evening sex better, and I like having something to look forward to. So, once he was finished, I swallowed his ejaculate, licked my lips, and got dressed for work. The perfect solution, don't you think?"

There's one other particular time during which some couples find fellatio and cunnilingus an especially practical and pleasurable alternative to sexual intercourse. This is during pregnancy and after the birth of a baby. It's pretty easy to see why regulation sex can become more and more uncomfortable as the abdomen of the mother-to-be grows larger. Frequently, when one or both partners are desirous of gratification, they will choose oral sex at this time. Also, once the baby is born, the usual medical recommendation is to avoid sexual intercourse until after the doctor gives the new mother his okay at her six-week check-up. But this doesn't mean no sexual pleasure is allowed. Margie, a friend of ours, told us this story: "A little more than a week after my baby was born, I was beginning to feel like myself again. That is, I thought I might be in the mood for sexual satisfaction, even though I knew intercourse was off-limits for the time being. Anyway, I was still sore. But my husband was more than willing to provide me with the most delightful oral session I can remember. Then I gave him a blow job he really enjoyed. All of this intimacy had the bonus of bringing us really close, and reminded us that we were still a couple, not just someone's parents. And even after my check-up, when it was perfectly okay to resume intercourse, we found ourselves enjoying the oral version more than ever. Guess we're just lucky."

Shy women with a strict upbringing may actually want to lead up to viewing the penis in gradual steps.

When Jacqueline and I hear stories like these, we realize what a long way this generation has travelled from the days when the techniques of oral sex were learned furtively, if at all. People today watch explicit videos, read readily available manuals, and talk freely with their friends about their personal sex practices, sharing tips and ideas that can only add to everyone's sexual enjoyment. Because of this liberal attitude, today more adults have an opportunity to explore and express their own normal sexuality, and to become emotionally healthy, instead of confused, embarrassed, and repressed.

It is a comforting fact to both of us that at any given moment in the world today, genital kissing is being performed with greater frequency and more willingly with less hesitation or guilt, than ever before. Since today's young people approach oral sex with much more open attitudes than their parents, they will certainly engage in it more often. We feel that finding pleasure in this way can lead only to good results. Oral sex freely indulged, for all those who want it, is a goal devoutly to be sought — and in the forefront of the seekers are today's generation of American young people. It's a healthy omen for the future.

Chapter Two
ADVANCED TECHNIQUES

We've told you about ourselves, Steven and Jacqueline — all about our oral sex techniques — how we got started and how we have developed and expanded them. You have gathered by now that we're enthusiastic devotees of the oral mode; we believe it's the greatest. And *you* must have at least a fairly strong interest in the subject or you wouldn't have read our book almost to its conclusion.

In the previous chapter we've taken a look at the practice of orality among young people — how it used to be, and how it is today. We've cited the cases of a number of young men and women and quoted their opinions and feelings. Now to make our study complete, let's hear from some adults other than ourselves who have been indulging in oral sex for some time and who find today's ready acceptance of offbeat sex practices, including orality, a very rewarding and fulfilling part of their lives. Following are a couple of case histories dated about six or eight years ago, and coming right up to the present. First, let's let George, a 28 year old East Coast salesman, tell his story (as recorded on our tapes):

I've got to say that my wife Dottie has a real knack for going down on me. I almost said blowing me but, of course, that isn't exactly what it is. For one thing, she really loves me and she's interested in pleasing *me,* not just gobbling it up to please herself.

I've always had a pretty active sex-life, never had any problem getting laid, and I've found that most girls will go down on you. From what I hear from older men that wasn't true a generation ago, at least not with *nice* girls — but it sure as hell has been true in *my* sex-life over the past seven years or so. I guess it's the "Sexual Revolution." Oh, a lot of them may be sort of hesitant at first, but if you have any kind of thing going with a girl that lasts for a while, eventually you can get damn near any one of them to blow you — I mean go down on you.

Of course, you can't get away from the fact that *some* girls just aren't with it — they haven't got it. First of all, some of them are really repelled by the idea of putting *that thing* in their dainty mouths. With them there's no use forcing the issue. But most of the time if you can just persuade a woman to do down for the first time, she'll usually find out — much to her surprise — that she really likes it. I honestly figure I've done some women a real favor by teaching them that there's a lot of fun to be had by going

Any position that makes the throat
perpendicular to the penetrating
penis will make deep throat fellatio
easier to accomplish.

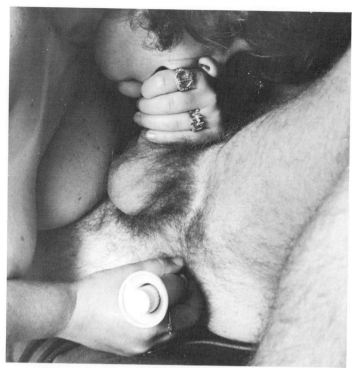

It is possible for the vibrator to penetrate the anal sphicter, but it should be lubricated prior to insertion.

The inner thighs are an erogenous zone with the nerve pathways that help stimulate the vulva.

down on a guy. And then, of course, there are the ones who've always secretly wanted to do it, but were too embarrassed. All they need is a little encouragement. They're just waiting for you to invite them to go down on that lovable pecker of yours.

I'll never forget this one young lady a few years ago; let's call her Cathy. I had a thing going with her for three or four months and I thought maybe we'd get married but it didn't work out that way. Cathy wasn't a virgin when I met her, but she wasn't very experienced. She was a beautiful woman. Her measurements were about 38-26-36 or something like that — and her face — wow, I couldn't describe what it did to me when she just looked at me *that* way!

We seemed to hit it off right from the start. Actually I met her on a bus one day. We were sitting next to each other and we got to talking, and we got off at the same stop and walked down the street together. And that was it. We didn't waste any time. Oh, it was maybe the third or fourth date before we went to bed together, but that was par for the course with a girl like Cathy.

We were sitting in her apartment drinking a nightcap, not saying much, just enjoying each other's company. We'd already kissed each other a few times and thoroughly enjoyed it — but we were so much at ease together that we didn't have to be touching or kissing every minute we had the chance. This night the mood was just right; we were both relaxed, she sitting in a chair and I

This position allows the woman literally to rub the vulva into the man's lips.

The woman is the active partner in the position shown. A rolling motion from the hips is more effective than up and down gyrations.

on the couch; there was soft music playing on the stereo. We sat looking into each other's eyes for a while. Then, as if somebody had given us the signal, we both stood up at the same moment and moved toward each other. I folded her in my arms, we kissed slowly and deeper. Our tongues entwined, and our bodies pressed closer and tighter together. We stood that way for a long time, then by mutual consent, still without a word, we moved into the bedroom and slowly undressed each other.

Naked, with one accord we fell across the bed and lay in each other's arms, locked in a deep warm kiss that went on and on. My hands roved over her luscious body, trailing across her belly to her thighs, roaming, never in a hurry — and her hands were doing the same to me. Finally I probed gently at her snatch and found the lips wet and ready. There was still no hurry, and I moved slowly over on top of her and found her pussy with my stiff prick. It sank right in, gradually and naturally, gripped tightly by the moist, heated walls of her snatch, and as it went in she whispered, "Yes! oh, yesssss ..." very quietly.

Those were the only words spoken the whole time. I exerted only a little pressure, letting my prick just sink in until it was all the way in. Well, I won't go into all the details of just what we did in that first fuck since you're supposed to be interviewing me about the oral part of it, right? Anyway, soon I felt my climax beginning slowly, deep down in my balls. I looked at her questioningly, looked into her half-closed eyes in that dim light, and she nodded silently and began to breathe faster. Then I was spurting deep inside her, and she groaned once and clasped me more tightly, as little shudders swept over her.

Well, that was the first time, and it shows you the kind of relationship we had. We screwed every night after that, and it was always the same. Oh, we were more frantic in our action sometimes, maybe almost violent. But that close feeling of *togetherness,* of mutual trust, was always there, and we were totally at ease with each other.

The only time even a little shadow of tension entered was the first time I asked Cathy to go down on me. Usually we hardly spoke at all while we were screwing. Oh, sure, there might be a few terms of endearment and so forth, but we had such unspoken communication between us that instructions and requests were never called for. Even when *I* went down on *her* — ate her cunt for the first time — which had never happened to her before, it came about naturally after I'd been tongue-bathing her body for maybe half an hour. She told me later that she'd always thought the very idea of having her cunt lapped

A chair or couch can become very useful to enhance your favorite approach to intercourse. The bed should never be regarded as the only place to make love.

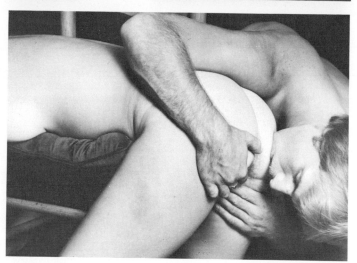

102

would disgust her but when it happened, she experienced only delight.

Anyway, one day we were lying in bed necking, and she began nipping me, giving me little love-bites all over my chest and belly. Then she licked me all over, along my belly and down to my thighs, and then back across my chest.

Very gently I pressed down on her head, trying to get her back down there and blow me. But she raised her head up and looked at me. 'I'm sorry, George,' she said, 'but I just *can't* do it. I want to, but I just *can't...*'

'Come here, honey,' I said softly, and folded her close against me. I stroked her hair and just held her until I felt the tension leave her body. Then we lay quietly for a few minutes. Finally I whispered, 'Honey, you don't *have* to do it, but it would mean a lot to me. Please at least try, won't you? You can stop any time you want.'

Suckling a man's testicles, if done gently, can be one of the most pleasurable experiences of his life.

The use of a small vibrator on a woman while orally manipulating her vagina brings increased stimulation.

She didn't say anything, but my tone must have been just right, because she didn't tense up either. After a moment she began kissing my chest again, nibbling on my nipples, then moving down to my crotch. She raised up her head for a second, looking down at my erect prick. Then she stuck her little pink tongue out and tentatively licked at the head. I think she was a little startled when it twitched in response. But she kept on. She started running her tongue up and down the shaft and around the knob. finally she formed an 'O' with her lips and suddenly engulfed the whole head and half the shaft with her hot, wet mouth.

I usually have pretty good control, but I damn near shot off right then! It was the most exciting thing I'd ever experienced in my whole sex-life. Her long blonde hair was fanned out softly over my belly and tickling my balls, and she instinctively applied just the right amount of

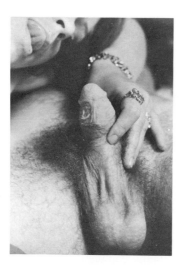

Studies have shown that some people are naturally orally oriented and that these people more than others use their mouth as a sense organ.

The so-called erotic trance is vital to achieving pleasure from sexual stimulation; while in the trance-like state of arousal, mind and body combine to create pleasure sensations.

pressure as she leaned against my body and sucked my prick.

She began moving her head up and down the shaft, darting her tongue around, and I had to tell her to take it easy. 'Go slow, baby, I'm almost there!' I panted. But she gripped my ass more tightly and increased the suction of her mouth, and at the same time she went down even further, so that the head was in her throat, down by her tonsils, and she began moving up and down faster and faster.

That was all it took. I couldn't hold it any longer. I shot off like a cannon — and would you believe, she didn't stop her furious sucking till my climax was all spent and my prick was going limp. Then she raised up and looked at me. She grinned impishly. 'You've got to admit, George, that was pretty good for a beginner!'

'Pretty good?' I exclaimed. 'Honey, it was absolutely fantastic!'

...Well, you people asked me to talk about cocksucking, about having my cock sucked, and now I've damn near told you my life story! But the point is that a lot of girls who are hesitant at first about sucking a prick learn to like it pretty damn quickly. Cathy was unusual, she began licking it — *loving* it — the first moment my cock was in her mouth. And she cared enough for me to concentrate on doing it just *right* the first time. She sensed and understood just how to give me the utmost pleasure. And she sure as hell enjoyed it herself. I forgot to mention that she came off by herself, had an orgasm without my help or

without even fingering herself, while she was sucking on me. I could tell by the way her hips jerked.

This went on for some months. When we finally parted, which we did just as gently and lovingly as we did everything else, Cathy had become a damn good cocksucker. The only gal I've ever known who is better than Cathy is Dottie, my wife, whom I met a few months after Cathy and I stopped seeing each other.
But that's another story..."

George's account has been quoted at length because it contains valuable lessons for the oral sex devotee. It demonstrates a type of relationship, sexual and emotional, that is unfortunately somewhat rare. George and Cathy quite obviously both had a natural bent toward oralism. George was already practicing it and Cathy needed only a nudge. But the thing that made their relationship so beautiful and rewarding was their simple *togetherness,* their mutual closeness. And let's not forget to credit an assist to the increasingly liberated sex mores of the past decade which have made such relationships possible among more and more people. Loving couples can now indulge freely and enthusiastically in oral sex without any of the guilts, fears, and inhibitions that beset people in former times.

And now to wind up our study, to make it complete, is a graphic account of cunnilingual pleasures, as told to Jacqueline and Steven by Harvey, a 27-year-old Arizona engineer, once again, a happily married man:

Many people believe that oral loving is the supreme physical expression of love.

...Actually, I don't know just where to begin. Roz and I indulge in a lot of variety in our lovemaking, and there are so many incidents involving cuntlapping, cunnilingus, that it's hard to pick one for this interview. Maybe I should tell you about an incident that happened recently. I was out of town on business for a couple of weeks, the first time we'd been separated for that long. When I got back we were both pretty worked-up.

Roz met me at the airport, and in the car in the parking lot we started necking like a couple of teenagers. There were quite a few people around, but we ignored them and really went at it. Roz had gotten into the driver's seat because I was tired and didn't feel like driving. As soon as I got in the other side I slid over and put my arms around her.

Our lips met in a hot, clinging kiss. Our tongues began their mutual dance and I got a hard-on immediately. I've got to admit, when we kissed like that, our wet mouths tearing at each other, I couldn't help but imagine I was chewing on her delicious cunt! I put my hand on Roz's tit and squeezed. She moaned and pressed against my hand while her own hand went down my crotch and squeezed my prick. We sat like that, pressed together and breathing

As orgasm approaches muscle strength increases providing ability to assume and maintain positions otherwise fatiguing.

heavily for a few minutes, then I panted: 'For God's sake, let's get out of here!' We pulled apart, and Roz started the car and drove out of the parking lot. It was about a 45-minute drive home, and I was so hot I didn't know how I could wait that long. I decided not to.

I turned my body and rested my right hand on Roz's thigh as she drove, running it up and down her leg, then dipping into the area between her legs, to feel her throbbing pussy and probe at her rectum through the panty material. She was panting like a locomotive. Finally I slipped my hand down inside the front of her panties and cupped the hot, soft mound in my hand, letting one finger run up and down the crease.

I admit we were acting like kids, but we were pretty damn horny and we didn't care — at least, *I* didn't. Roz moaned: 'Harvey, how am I supposed to drive with you getting me all hot and bothered?'

'Well, stop driving,' I said, 'and you won't have to worry!'

'Don't tempt me! We'd look pretty silly screwing at the side of the road...'

But I kept right on and she didn't protest any more — she just breathed harder and faster and wiggled her legs. She spread her thighs a little more and squirmed in the seat. In a minute or so we had to stop for a red light, and I said: 'Raise up, honey, so I can get these damn panties off!'

She lifted herself up four or five inches, and I got the panties down around her knees. Then I slipped off her garterbelt and peeled her nylons down. I slipped the panties over her feet — but then the light turned green and she had to start driving again.

Her garter-belt was down around her knees, with the nylons peeled down part-way, and she looked sexy as hell driving along like that. At the next stoplight I took off her shoes and pulled the stockings off her feet while she moaned in faint protest. I pushed the back of her skirt up behind her so that her bare ass was on the seat-cover; and the skirt barely covered her pussy.

Roz was driving sort of erratically now. Her mind clearly wasn't on it. I kept both hands on her thighs. When we got to the highway which was dark and not much traveled at that hour, I unbuttoned her blouse and pulled it out of her skirt. She leaned forward and I managed to get her bra unfastened. Using the expert technique I'd learned I forget where, I got the bra all the way off without removing her blouse.

Her tits were open to me now. They were still covered by the thin loose blouse but I could get at them and I did. Moving one hand back down to her legs and then to her pussy, I lifted one tit in my other hand and sucked it between my lips, biting the nipple lightly with my teeth.

Roz was moaning, squirming, and jerking spasmodically. She could hardly drive. The car was jumping along

The entire skin area around the vulva can be sensitized by fingers, mouth or the use of sex toys.

A successful fellatrice uses her hands to control and guide the penis and her mouth to pleasure it.

107

the highway in fits and starts. 'Stop it, Harvey! she moaned. 'Stop, or I'll lose control of the car! We'll crack up!'

Reluctantly I desisted. I sat up, sighed, and looked out the window for a few minutes just resting one hand on her thigh without moving it. Then in a few minutes, when she'd calmed down a bit, I pulled her right knee toward me. Then I bent my head and licked at her pussy. She gave in this time. She pushed her left leg against the driver's door to make it easier for me, but I still couldn't get my head into the proper position to do a good job eating her pussy. I did the best I could, however, running my tongue up and down between the lips of her pussy and occasionally flicking her clitoris with the tip of my tongue.

I didn't do too good a job, but it wasn't too bad. We were both hot as hell by the time she pulled the car into our home driveway. I stuffed her scattered things into the pocket of my jacket. I didn't even take my suitcase out of the car-trunk. We got out of the car and dashed to the

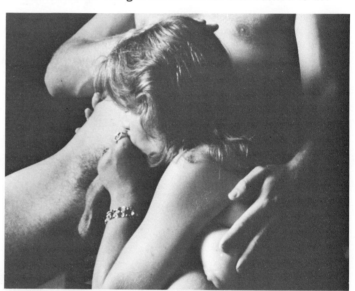

Some couples feel guilt about performing oral love to climax although there is no rational basis for such guilt.

108

The speed and intensity of a man's arousal are increased if he watches the woman masturbate as she fellates him.

With the labial lips pulled apart, the tongue has complete access to every portion of the labial groove.

In some women, the breasts are so sensitive that they rival the vulva as the center of erotic feeling.

front door like a couple of kids running to get out of the rain. The minute the door was closed behind us, I grabbed Roz and kissed her fiercely. The kiss was so hard and hot and had such an effect on us that we sank to the floor together right there in the hallway.

'Get naked, Harvey!' she gasped. She threw her blouse off and then slipped out of her skirt. I stood up and yanked off my clothes; she helped me by going to work on my shoes and pants. In a few seconds I was as naked as she was. My prick was hot and throbbing, and her pussy ground against it so deliciously that I was afraid I'd come right then and there — but I managed to hold myself in.

My mouth was all over her as I pulled her down to the floor. I licked her from the bottom of her tiny feet right up to her forehead, licking everywhere except inside her snatch. Then I worked my way back down, spending lots

Those couples who regularly
practice analingus discover there
are as many different ways of using
the tongue on the anus as on the sex
organs.

In this position the pressure of her
leg on the man's neck and
shoulders will vary in a direct ratio to
the pleasure he produces.

of time on her tits, and then across her belly to her thighs. I
licked all around her pussy without touching the slit itself,
letting my tongue dwell on the little crease between her
thighs and her cunt.

Finally I knew Roz couldn't stand it any more. She was
writhing wildly on the carpet, bucking her hips, and
moaning. Her cunt was wet as a dishrag. 'Do it *now,*
Harvey!' she pleaded. 'Eat me *now!* Please!' But I kept
licking around her inner cunt-lips, her *labia minora,* back
and forth, around and around, and once in a while I'd nip
the lips lightly, driving her frantic as I well knew.

Then I switched the action. I hit her clit with the tip of my
tongue, then I sucked it into my mouth like a nipple, and
ran my tongue all around it. Roz's hips bucked up against
my chin and she was moaning steadily now. Finally I stuck
my tongue inside, tasting the hot inner walls, exploring the
pulsating wrinkles of her vagina.

Roz was going wild now and I couldn't blame her. I was
so hot that if she had touched my prick I'd have shot my
wad immediately. Then she started tensing up, holding
her hips up off the floor, and her rhythmic moans became
louder and faster.   Just a few more seconds now and
she'd come, I knew from experience. But I was too
impatient to wait any longer. I suddenly raised up over her
and plunged my prick right into her gaping hole. We were
both too far gone to fiddle around any longer. I slid it all the

110

A woman may enjoy contemplating the effect she has on the penis and find her own arousal in the contemplation.

Despite the fact that passion increases physical capabilities, positions that are awkward or create physical strain for one partner should be subtly altered by the other.

way in on the first stroke — and the moment it was deep inside, I blew the biggest load I'd done in years. Roz came too, digging her nails into my shoulders and biting my neck. Then she raised her face up to me and we mashed our lips and tongues together in a long, fiery kiss while our juices mingled in a magnificent orgasm.

We lay there for half an hour before we could get up and go into the bedroom. We spent the rest of the night in each other's arms, eating and fucking, fucking and eating. She ate me as much as I ate her, maybe more. We finally stopped, worn out, about seven in the morning."

The point to note in Harvey's vivid story is his and Roz's willingness to act "like a couple of kids," even though they were mature, responsible adults. It is only the person who is *free* enough inside himself or herself to enjoy such "childish" delights who can be called really mature and secure. There are still too many people who simply can't let themselves go, as Harvey and Roz did. They are two fine people whose sex-life is obviously well adjusted — and this adjustment carries over into the other areas of their life together.

AFTERWORD

In the previous pages, we have covered many details of the genital kissing experience in a way not commonly encountered in the literature on the subject. We find oral sex between us an extremely pleasurable experience, and we have approached the writing of this book from that point of view. Oral sex is *fun*. Sex should be enjoyed as pure pleasure by those individuals engaging in it.

We do not urge anyone to perform *any* sex acts against his or her will because coercion immediately removes the pleasure and makes it, if not extremely onerous, at least a chore.

What we hope you will do is to approach oral sex with an open mind and an open mouth, expecting to receive from it a high degree of pleasure. Approaching it with a positive attitude you will undoubtedly succeed, for the only failures in genital kissing are self-induced. We want to repeat that there is no higher expression of love that you can offer your partner than caressing his or her body with your lips and tongue. We have belabored this idea so many times throughout this book that it may indeed be redundant repeating it here, but it is an idea we hold so strongly that we feel it cannot be emphasized enough.